One Moment

One Moment

Becky Hunter

CORVUS

Published in hardback in Great Britain in 2023 by Corvus, an imprint of
Atlantic Books Ltd.

10 9 8 7 6 5 4 3 2 1

A CIP catalogue record for this book is available from the British Library.

Hardback ISBN: 978 1 83895 866 4
Trade paperback ISBN: 978 1 83895 867 1
E-book ISBN: 978 1 83895 868 8

Printed in Great Britain by TJ Books Limited

Corvus
An imprint of Atlantic Books Ltd
Ormond House
26–27 Boswell Street
London
WC1N 3JZ

www.corvus-books.co.uk

ONE MOMENT

Prologue

Evie sat on her towel, hands pressed into the white sand behind her, long legs stretched out, her skin embarrassingly luminescent under the bright sun. It was still early enough that the beach wasn't packed with tourists, but already the thrum of life was making itself known. Umbrellas and sunbeds were being set up, kids were splashing in the warm waves, couples were chatting in low tones as they strolled hand-in-hand along the shoreline.

And Scarlett. Over and above it all there was Scarlett, emerging from the water. She was totally pulling off the beachy, surfer-girl look, her blonde hair looking more wavy than scraggly, blue eyes made even bluer by the colour of the ocean. They'd come on holiday with a group of friends from school, but Evie and Scarlett had snuck out first thing, just the two of them, while everyone else was still in bed after a heavy night.

'What are you doing sitting down?' Scarlett said as she approached Evie.

Evie tilted her head back, sunglasses protecting her from the glare of the sun, to look at her.

'We're supposed to be making the most of every moment,' Scarlett insisted. 'We're only here for a week.'

'I *am* making the most of it,' Evie said, spreading her arms wide. 'This is what I want to be doing.' Sitting, enjoying the sun on a beach in Crete, celebrating the end of school – could it get any better than that?

Scarlett put her hands on her hips as she looked around the beach, her gaze almost assessing. Then she gave a decisive nod, like the beach had passed some kind of test. 'This is the perfect send-off,' she said, her lips pulling into a satisfied smile.

Send-off. Evie supposed that was right. She remembered what Scarlett had told her last week, when they'd got their A-Level results. *It's only up from here.* And it was, wasn't it? They were going to different universities, but both of them were in Manchester, like they'd planned. Evie was off to study music, Scarlett to study fashion. *The start of the rest of their lives*, Scarlett had said, eyes holding the kind of fervour that was impossible to argue with. Admittedly there was a part of Evie that couldn't help feeling anxious. That wondered what would happen if they didn't make it – if they weren't as successful as Scarlett insisted they would be – but she was trying her best to squash that feeling down.

'We're going to have the best lives, Eves.' Scarlett laughed and threw her hands in the air. 'The best lives!' She started twirling, blonde hair flying, not caring that everyone on the beach was watching her. Evie watched too, a smile pulling at her lips.

Then Scarlett grabbed Evie's hand, pulled her up from the ground and Evie laughed as she joined in, spinning round and round on the sand. She closed her eyes, pretended there was no one else there, that it was just her and Scarlett. And in that moment she decided it didn't matter, anyway. It didn't matter if things didn't go exactly as planned, if their dreams had to change. Because as long as they had each other, they'd be okay.

Chapter One

The morning that I die I'm in a rush to leave the flat. I couldn't get to sleep last night, too on edge, replaying what happened earlier in the evening, my stomach curdling with anxiety, so I slept through the alarm. Now I can't find the bloody key, we've run out of instant coffee and I don't have time to make a proper one. I check the time on my phone as I scurry into our tiny kitchen and swear – silently, so I don't wake Evie. I have a meeting near Borough Market first thing, and at this rate I'm going to miss it. It's not like I can ring, push it back. The whole bloody day is backlogged up to the party this evening, which I have to be on form for, because Jason has got these investors interested in my idea for a new label.

My mind immediately turns to Jason then. No. I'm not thinking about him. I'm not. I promised myself I wouldn't – for this morning at least. Besides, Jason isn't the point of the party. These people, they are interested in *me*. My idea. I want to use recyclable materials, which is very on trend at the moment, and they liked my designs too, the 'boldness' of them apparently. It would be so cool. To create something all my own. It will make all of the long hours, the shit pay, the endless fawning over people more important than me worth it.

I stop looking through the fruit bowl for my keys – I know it sounds obscure, but Evie once found them there – and take a breath. Evie can let me in later. I spin round on the fake terracotta tiles – really they are just plastic, and the edges are peeling away in the corners and where the cupboards meet the floor – and reach for the whiteboard and pen that Evie keeps stuck to the fridge. It's one of those magnetic pads; she picked it up for us a few years ago because I kept losing all the Post-it notepads. It's a tradition for us to write notes to each other. It started when we first moved to London together. I was working as an intern, which basically meant no money and endless hours, and Evie was out temping whilst also auditioning for all those amateur orchestras, so we hadn't been in the flat together at the same time much and Evie had started the notes. A way to make us both feel less lonely, and to keep each other up to date.

She doesn't do it much any more. Some days I know she finds writing too difficult, other times I think she simply doesn't have anything to say – the days when she can't bring herself to leave the flat. Occasionally, on good days, she'll write something or do a little drawing, and I know it's to convince me that she's okay. But mostly she leaves it to me.

The same photos are still stuck to the fridge from when Evie and I first moved in. Us on the beach in Crete, just after we finished A Levels, grinning like loons with our arms around each other. Me holding a champagne bottle – one that Evie had bought for me after I finished my degree. Us at my twenty-first, surrounded by a group of

6

people we've mainly lost touch with today. There used to be a photo of Evie at her graduation too, holding her violin, but she tore it down on a bad day about six months ago. Looking at the photos makes my stomach lurch, thinking of last night. I went too far, I know I did.

Trying to push that aside, I take the whiteboard and rest it on the countertop, in between the fruit bowl – which, incidentally, never has any fruit in it – and the pile of washing up. I should have cleared it up last night really, but after the argument I'd stormed straight into my room. The chopping board covered in crumbs, knife coated in butter and leftover cereal bowls stare at me accusingly and I have to look away.

Don't worry about the washing up, I scrawl on the whiteboard, *I'll do it later.* I stop. Maybe she'll take that the wrong way, assume it's because I think she can't do it or something. Especially after last night. I rub out the words, start again. *I'll be back late this evening, so don't wait up. Big night!! I'll message, let you know how it goes. But curry and wine tomorrow, yeah?* I leave it at that. No point trying to put everything down on a whiteboard. We'll talk tomorrow, and it'll be fine. There is nothing Evie and I can't fix, surely.

I put the cap back on the pen and head out of the kitchen to the adjoining living room. It's as I'm crossing the threshold from plastic tiles to old beige carpet that something slices into the sole of my foot and I swear, loudly. I bring my foot up, see blood seeping through my black tights, along with a tiny shard of glass, glinting in the artificial light of the flat. I hobble to the sofa to pick the shard out, placing it on the little coffee table. A memory of last night flashes into my mind – one of our glasses smashing across the floor in the kitchen, water and glass going everywhere. Evie and I staring at it, until Evie made a stiff movement towards the cupboard under the sink, where we keep the dustpan and brush.

'I'll do it,' I said quickly.

'It's fine,' Evie said, through gritted teeth.

'But I—'

'I said it's fine, okay!'

I glance at Evie's door. I should check on her, I know I should. But I'm already late, and I don't know how long that conversation will end up taking. I need to get going. I *want* to get going – there is so much to look forward to today.

I stand up, ignoring the prick in my foot, shove my long black boots on and grab my handbag from where I've dumped it by the front door. I love this handbag. I saved up all through my degree to get it. It's a beautiful crocodile print by a designer who was up-and-coming at the time – a talking point for future interviews.

I'm opening the front door when I hear the click of Evie's bedroom door. I look over my shoulder at her. She's always pale, but she looks paler than normal today, with dark shadows under her eyes. She's wearing flannel pyjama bottoms along with that ugly T-shirt of Will's that she still wears to bed, even though the bastard left her. She's looking at me a little warily, and I imagine I look the same to her. The residue of last night's argument making itself known.

She's got headphones on and she slips them off her head, flushes slightly. She pretends that she doesn't listen to music any more — at least the type of music I know she loves. That's why she's always listening on headphones, rather than playing it out loud in her room, because she doesn't want to admit that she's doing it. I know she does, though, and *she* knows I know, but neither of us says anything about it. It's a thing.

'You're leaving?' The slight accusation in her voice sends an unpleasant jolt through me. It is too close to what she said last night.

I clear my throat. 'Yeah. I left you a note.' I gesture towards the kitchen, but Evie keeps looking directly at me.

'I thought you were starting later today, because of the party?'

'I am.' Why do I sound so formal? This is *Evie*, for Christ's sake. I hate this. Evie and I don't fight, not really. She is the constant in my life — I *need* her to be the constant in my life. But I can't think of what to say to make it better, not in the timeframe I've got.

She's still waiting for an answer, arms crossed over her chest. There's a moment here when I could tell the truth — what I'm doing this morning, and why. But it's the wrong time. The argument is still too fresh for both of us, and I don't have time to explain properly. So I lie. 'I have to go in early to work, start the prep.' The words taste bitter on my tongue.

She nods slowly, while I do a quick scan of her, up and down. Assessing, in the way I've got used to doing over the past two years or so, trying to check if she's okay, to figure out what kind of day she might be having. Evie narrows her eyes, and I know she's clocked what I'm doing.

'Are you coming to the party later?' I ask quickly.

'Maybe,' Evie says after a beat. 'I'll let you know, is that all right?' She's too stiff. Is she regretting last night too? Probably – she hates losing her temper.

'Of course.' I doubt she'll come. She rarely comes out these days. Though tonight is important for me, so maybe she'll surprise me. Or maybe not, after last night. The anxiety curdles again in my stomach.

A message beeps on my phone and I scramble in my handbag for it. My heart spasms in that way that is both pain and pleasure when I see who it is. Jason.

Meet me before you go into work today. I want to see you. Not a question, but then that's not really Jason's style. Another message follows: **I'll be at the Soho flat until eleven.**

I feel the heat flash through me, the way I've never been able to control around him, but I drop the phone back in my handbag. I tell myself I won't go, that I'll stick firm to the line I've drawn there.

Evie is still looking at me. She doesn't comment, but I wonder if she suspects who the message is from. Probably. We've never been able to hide anything from one another – never usually wanted to. Out of everyone in the world, Evie is the one person I could tell anything to, and I know she feels the same.

'I've got to go,' I say, because I really do.

10

Her eyes flare then. That sparky anger lighting up the green. I've always admired her eyes, how expressive they are. It's the one place she can't hide her anger, even though I know she tries.

'I'll see you later, okay?' I try to make my voice upbeat, to pretend that nothing is going on here, but I can see the bitterness, from the way she keeps her face so straight, the way her arms tighten around her. She does not want me to leave. Maybe she doesn't want me to leave her here, alone, or maybe she thinks I should stay until we sort this out, have a proper conversation.

But she nods, and I take that as permission. Because I do have to go – the day is calling to me. And I need time, to figure out what to say, how to make this better. I make the effort to flash her a quick smile before I step out into the musty-smelling corridor of the first floor of our block of flats, where the light seems to be endlessly flickering.

'Scar?' She calls my name as I'm shutting the door, and I pull it wider again so that I can look in at her. 'I…' She blows out a breath. 'Nothing.' The *nothing* echoes in the space between us. She doesn't know what to say either, does she? Why should she? She might have ended up saying something she regretted, but I was the one who pushed last night, so I'm the one who needs to make it better. It's a pattern between us: I make the mistake, I plead for forgiveness and Evie forgives me. I just have to figure out how, exactly, to plead this time. *Later*, I tell myself. I need to get today out of the way – there's a lot that can change in one day, after all.

11

'Good luck today, yeah?' Evie continues. 'I'm sure you'll be great – it'll be your Melanie Griffiths in *Working Girl* moment.'

I smile for real then. Because she's deliberately breaking the tension between us, offering me an olive branch. 'Or Reese Witherspoon in *Legally Blonde*?'

Evie cocks her head, her long dark hair spilling to one side. 'No one ever doubted you could do it, though, did they?'

'I haven't done it yet,' I say gruffly.

Evie smiles, a little sadly. I'm not sure how to read it, that sadness. Maybe that, in comparison to her, I'm on the way to achieving my dream, whereas she… 'You have. Even if this doesn't come off, which I think it will, you still will have.'

My feet start tapping, impatient for the rest of me to get moving. 'Eves, I'm so sorry but I really do have to—'

'Go. I know.' She waves a hand in the air, gesturing me on my way. 'I'll be fine.' She says it firmly and I feel sure, in that moment, that it's a promise. That Evie and I are stronger than one argument; that, no matter what, we will stick together, as we always have done.

But I don't get a chance to test that theory, do I?

Chapter Two

I shove my hands into my coat pockets as I walk along Borough High Street, protecting them from the biting chill that has captured April. Despite the cold, it's bright, the sun shining out of a clear blue sky, and the day seems almost hopeful. I suppose that's ironic, really, given what happens next.

I've caught up with myself in terms of time, with the first thing on my to-do list already ticked off, but that doesn't stop me walking quickly, my boots clicking along the pavement, joining in the morning chaos of London. Rush hour is officially over, but everyone in London seems to be perpetually in a hurry. It's part of why I love this city. I love the unpredictability of it, the constant movement, never knowing who or what might be around the corner.

Because I left the flat without one this morning, I head into the nearest coffee shop and order a black Americano. I taught myself to like black coffee years ago, when I first started my degree. There are no calories in it, and I have to stay slim for work. I'd rather have one of the Easter-themed drinks, full of sugar and cream and yumminess, that are still on sale despite the fact that Easter was last weekend. No point in wasting the calories on it, I tell myself firmly.

I briefly smile at the slightly harried-looking guy –

young, early twenties, I'd guess – behind the counter, before getting out my phone, scrolling through WhatsApp automatically. Someone bumps into me and I scowl, but don't bother looking up to see who it is. I've got a little immune to it, I think, from years of taking the Tube – getting bumped into is par for the course here.

My fingers linger over the message from Jason. I know, I know, I promised myself I wouldn't think of him, but he's going to be at the party and I can't just ignore him. Well, theoretically I could. I could also not go to the flat, pretend I never saw the message, and when we see each other this evening he'll no doubt be the perfect example of professionalism. No one will notice the looks he sends me across the room. No one will notice the way I smile at him, because I'm a shameless flirt and I smile at everyone like that.

Fuck, I want to see him. I want to go to that flat. I shouldn't, I really shouldn't. But I do.

'Black Americano!' The way the guy shouts it makes me realize it's not the first time he's said it, and I shove my phone back in my bag – without replying to Jason. I take the paper cup, annoyed at myself for forgetting the reusable takeaway cup that Evie got me for Christmas last year. We started doing stockings for each other when we first moved to London and although the presents were pretty crap at first, relying mainly on charity shops, the last couple of years we've actually put some decent stuff in there, coffee mug included. It's unashamedly garish – bright pink and purple with silver writing that says, 'Bring on the Sparkle'.

It's so ridiculous and every time I hand it over to baristas, they sort of do a double-take. I was slightly appalled when I first unwrapped it, I'll admit, and Evie burst out laughing at my expression. It was a reminder, according to her, not to take myself too seriously, because generally everything I own is carefully chosen, always on trend. The mug's not something I'd usually be seen dead with, and initially I used it solely to honour my friendship with Evie, but now, I have to admit, I bloody love it. Every time I get it out, it makes me smile, which I'm sure was Evie's intention.

Evie. Maybe I should ring her or message her, or something. Though she offered me the olive branch, it still feels odd that we didn't officially resolve anything. But no. I think – stupidly, it turns out – that I'll have time for that later. It's for the same reason that I don't answer the call from my mum when her name flashes on the screen. I know what it'll be about: my thirtieth birthday is coming up soon, and she wants to make a splash. I love her for it, I do, but I don't want to talk about that right now.

There is so much pressure: to have this big party, celebrate the end of your twenties. But I don't *want* to be at the end of my twenties, because I'm supposed to have everything sorted by this point, aren't I? And yes, work is good, and I love London, but there is so much that isn't sorted. Well, mainly my relationship status. It's stupid, I know, to get hung up on it. Evie isn't in a relationship, either, something that keeps me sane, but most of our school friends from back home are married off. My single colleagues and I reassure each other with the fact that London is different, that we don't have *time* for the dating apps. And sometimes that makes me feel better. But mostly I wonder what the hell I'm doing and why I haven't found someone yet. Because, let's be honest, Jason doesn't count.

I head back out of the café, take a sip of my coffee and grimace slightly at the bitterness. Ahead of me, the pedestrian crossing is counting down: three seconds left to get across. It's one of those perpetually busy crossroads where you have to cross one section of the road and then wait in the middle for ages until the lights change on the other side – unless you're one of those who has nailed the timings and can dash across before the cars start coming.

Usually I'm one of those who rush, so I don't have to waste precious seconds of my life waiting for the lights to change. So I don't know what it is today that makes me pause – pause for that second too long, so that I'm stuck on my side of the road, with two sets of lights to get through now.

I shift from foot to foot as the cars come too fast through the crossing. The cyclists come round too, zooming past in their green cycle lane. I watch as some guy on a bright-red bike careers around the corner. It's impossible not to notice him. Unlike the other kamikaze cyclists, he's not wearing Lycra. Instead he's in jeans and a jumper, marking him out as different. He's wearing no helmet, messy brown hair clearly on show.

He's also holding the handlebars with only one hand in the middle, the other pressing his phone to his ear. He's laughing, presumably at something the other person is saying, as he heads towards the lights where I'm standing. Maybe it's that which draws me to him, keeps my gaze focused on him as he shoots past me, running through the lights literally the second they turn from amber to red, without so much as checking over his shoulder.

The fact that I'm standing, watching as the lights change, means that I see it all. See the man flying through the lights at the wrong time. Watch as one of the oncoming cars from the other direction – potentially running their own red light at the last minute – beeps loudly. As the cyclist visibly jolts, swerves, still one-handed, then has to immediately swerve the other way, out of the cycle lane, as another car comes straight at him.

The green man is flashing, the lights beeping. I should be crossing the road now. But I'm still watching this man, now a few metres beyond me, to my left. Watching as he falls, head-first. And I'm holding my breath, because he doesn't get up. A couple of cars beep, but no one stops. No one on the pavement is moving, either – the classic bystander effect. Usually I, too, would leave it to someone else to sort out. That's the thing about London sometimes: there are so many people around to help, it means you don't have to.

But this time I jerk into action. Coffee spills through the small opening in the lid of my cup, heat searing my hand. I drop it completely, black liquid seeping across the tarmac.

I step off the pavement, into the cycle lane where he has landed. In hindsight, I'll wonder why I did it. Maybe it was the argument, still turning around my mind – if I was out in the world, living a life that Evie could not, then I

17

could at least do something useful while I was at it. Maybe I was thinking of the message from Jason, about the fact that I needed to face up to what I was doing – and so I felt I should try to reset the balance, good deeds versus bad. But at the time I'm not aware of any of those thoughts. I'm acting without really thinking about it.

When I get to him, his bike is strewn across the road, causing the passing cars to swerve around it, but he is still sprawled in the green cycle lane. I crouch down and the man groans. I feel a rush of relief. If he's groaning, I'm pretty sure he's not dead.

He looks up at me. He's got nice eyes. They're deep brown, like a dark mocha, and they seem warm. 'Are you okay?' I ask, as a car rushes past, beeping, like that will make the bike get out of its way. He nods and I hold out my hand, pull him to his feet. He grunts, and I brace against his weight. There is more beeping behind me. Can they not see there's been an accident?

Cyclists come swooping past now as, presumably, the lights change, and I pull the man to the side, out of harm's way. He frowns at me, and briefly I wonder if I should check for concussion. What are you supposed to do? Ask what day of the week it is? Who the prime minister is?

He looks around at the tarmac, dumbfounded, as if wondering how he ended up there. I glance down too, see his phone, completely smashed, lying a couple of metres away. After checking quickly for any oncoming cyclists, I dart to it, grab it off the ground. Hand it back to him.

'Thanks,' he says. 'And thanks for...' He tails off, gestures at himself, his bike, still lying a short distance away from us.

'You shouldn't be on the phone while you're riding your bike.' I say it primly, almost condescendingly, and I wrinkle my nose with how it sounds. Another car comes past, and I feel the wind it leaves in its wake whipping across my back.

The man's eyebrows shoot up, but he doesn't look offended. 'Suppose not.' Then he grins, a nice, easy expression, one that makes me instantly at ease: *infectious* is what I think to myself in that moment. He waves a hand to encompass his body – his face is scraped on one side, and his hands look like they are a little skinned too. 'Clearly not.'

I offer him a little apologetic smile, then, as he seems to be making no move to get it, I hurry into the road to grab his bike, timing it with the lights changing. I bend down to grab the handlebars, then hold it out to him. 'Sorry, what I meant to say was—'

It happens so quickly after that. Mid-sentence, my words stolen away from me. I barely register the change in his expression, the way he lurches towards me, out of the cycle lane and into the road, as if to grab me. He's not looking at me. That's my main thought, in the nanosecond that I have to think. That contorted, panicked expression isn't being caused by *me*, but by something behind me, over my shoulder.

I don't have time to turn, to see. I don't hear the brakes, the horn, the shouting. Not right away. Not until I'm already falling, already registering the pain. Hot and blind and all-encompassing. Across my torso as I'm sent flying, away from the car that hit me and back onto the tarmac.

Then my head. Something cracking, impossible pain shooting down the back of my skull, to my spine. My whole body reverberating with it.

But it's brief. Over before I know it.

I don't even realize what's happened, because I'm dead the second after I hit the pavement.

Chapter Three

Evie contemplated going back to bed the moment Scarlett left the flat. She hadn't slept well last night. Their shouting match had taken so much out of her, especially after a rough couple of weeks, but even though her bones ached with tiredness, even though her mind felt foggy, her body stayed resolutely awake, replaying what Scarlett had said to her. She felt the flash of anger, though she shoved it back down where it belonged. It was not fair to blame Scarlett. It was not Scarlett's fault.

She eyed her bed again. She knew, though, that if she crawled back under the covers, that would be it for the day and she'd never get anything done. Mornings were usually the best time of day for her, and she'd learned to try and make the most of them. So she made her bed instead.

She pulled on some clothes – leggings, a long-sleeved top and the woollen cardigan that Scarlett hated because it was so ugly, especially now, with a hole forming at the cuff of the sleeve. But there was no point in dressing up, was there? She wouldn't leave the house today, she'd already decided. Not that she felt awful. Not as bad as yesterday, and even that had been better than the day before. She gave an experimental wiggle of her toes, flexed her fingers, rolled her shoulders. She felt relief slide through her at the fact that her body seemed a little more her own today.

She shuffled out of her bedroom. She'd have to start work soon. She'd send a message to her boss, tell him she'd be working from home. Which he'd love, of course. Assistants weren't *meant* to work from home, according to him – because how could they do their jobs properly? How would they *learn* about the nuances of the advertising industry if they were sitting at home all day? He didn't care about that, though; he had no interest in Evie's career progression. What he actually meant was: how could she do the *personal* jobs for him, like buying presents for various family members and booking dinners for him and his wife? He'd been making noises about his and his wife's anniversary recently, and Evie knew she'd get dragged into that. It had only been pressure from HR that had made him agree to let her work from home at all – and even that, she imagined, wouldn't last for ever.

She clocked the note from Scarlett on the whiteboard when she got to the kitchen.

Big night!!

Evie stared at it, thinking about Scarlett inviting her to the party. About her answer. *Maybe.* It had been a lie, they'd both known that. But maybe she *should* go. Scarlett didn't always act like it, but Evie knew she was nervous. And after last night, would it mean something if she didn't show? Because ultimately she was being selfish, wasn't she? Refusing to go because *she* didn't want to, because *she'd* be uncomfortable, rather than choosing to go because her best friend needed her. Not that Scarlett had actually said she needed Evie there. Maybe she wouldn't even want her there – a burden on her big night, someone she'd have to look after. That was the problem really, wasn't it? Evie needed Scarlett more than Scarlett needed her.

It was as she was filling the kettle that she clocked it. Scarlett's house key, sitting behind one of the taps, the silver glint of it almost matching the grey sink. Honestly, why was her key *here*? She'd probably intended to start the washing up or something last night and dumped her key here at the same time. Evie should get her a bracelet with a key attachment on, so that she couldn't keep losing it.

She sighed and slipped her phone out of her leggings pocket, sent a quick text to Scarlett. She'd be assuming Evie would let her in later, of course, but who knew what time Scarlett would be back. If the evening went well, there would no doubt be celebratory drinks after the party, and in all likelihood Evie would be passed out by then.

A few minutes later and Scarlett still hadn't replied. Maybe she was still mad, after last night. Evie huffed at herself, picked up the phone. Stupid to sit around waiting for her to reply. They were adults, and this was her best friend. So she dialled Scarlett's number, leaned against the counter as she waited for her to answer.

'Hello?'

Evie jolted at the sound of a male voice. Low, but jerky somehow. A panicked sound. 'Hello,' she said cautiously. 'I'm looking for Scarlett.'

'Scarlett?' It was said with that same jerk, like a sharp intake of breath before the word was spoken out loud. In the background Evie could hear traffic and wind, causing static against the receiver. 'Right. Right, sorry. Fuck, sorry. Scarlett. She's... I'm sorry, how do you know her?'

Evie felt her grip tighten on her phone. 'I'm her friend. Evie. We live together.' She didn't quite know what made her add the last bit – a kind of justification, as to how well she knew Scarlett. 'Who are *you*? Why do you have Scarlett's phone?'

'I'm—' But someone that end cut him off.

'Sir? Are you coming with her?'

A hesitation, then, 'Yes. Yes, I'm—'

'Hello?' Evie said again, her voice louder, higher-pitched. 'Can I please just speak to Scarlett?'

Sirens. She only noticed them now. There were sirens in the background.

'Look, I'm so sorry, Evie, but Scarlett, she's...' The swallow was audible, and it made Evie's mouth go dry. 'She's had an accident.'

Evie stilled. She hadn't even noticed she'd been moving, shifting from foot to foot, impatiently flexing her fingers, until she stopped. A hot, painful tingle flared down the back of her spine. Her body, warning her.

'What do you mean, an accident?' Her voice didn't sound like hers.

'She's... Oh Jesus. Look, they're putting her in the ambulance now. I'm going to go with her, okay? They're taking her to Guy's Hospital. Near London Bridge.'

'London Bridge?' Evie repeated numbly. Her brain was working too slowly, refusing to catch up. She held on to the irrelevant information, the thing that she could let herself focus on. 'But Scarlett works in Soho.' And she'd said she was going to work, hadn't she? It made no sense for her to be in London Bridge. Did Jason live there? She didn't think so.

'I'm—'

She realized, too late, that this was not the point. That something very wrong was happening here. 'What accident?' she asked sharply. 'What's wrong with Scarlett? Can I speak to her?'

'She's…' A slightly choked sound then. One that made Evie's heart spasm, caused her to let out a noise like a whimper. 'I've got to go. I think… I think you'd better get to the hospital, Evie. I'm really sorry. God, I'm so sorry. I… I've got to go.'

He hung up. He actually hung up. Evie stood, her phone still pressed to her ear.

Scarlett, in an ambulance.

Scarlett, unable to talk to her.

What kind of accident would leave her unable to speak? No. She couldn't go down that road. She didn't know anything for sure. Her heart was speeding up now, fast, frantic beats. She needed to get to the hospital. She mustn't overreact. Scarlett would need her to be the calm one, the rational one.

She spurred herself into action, lurching towards her bedroom, pulling the first shoes she could find onto her feet, swearing as she got one arm stuck, trying to get her coat on. She dialled Scarlett's mum as she rushed around, gathering her keys, her purse.

'Hello, Evie love. I was just talking about you, saying to Graham that we should ring you. You know Scarlett's party, for her birthday—'

'Mel.' She tried for calm, but the word was too high, too scratchy. 'Scarlett's had an accident. She's in an ambulance. They're taking her to Guy's Hospital, near London Bridge.' Too fast. She was speaking too fast.

Calm, she told herself. But her body wouldn't listen.

'What?' Mel snapped. 'What kind of—'

'I don't know.' She snapped too. The panic coming to the fore. 'I'm sorry. I don't know. I got a call and I...'

'All right, okay. Graham!' Evie heard the rebound of Mel's voice, could imagine her in Scarlett's cottage, the one her parents never moved out of. 'We'll get on a train, meet you there. If you find out anything before we...'

'I'll let you know,' Evie said, hating the way her voice shook. What, exactly, would she have to let them know?

'She'll be okay,' Mel said firmly. 'This is Scarlett. She'll be okay.'

'Yeah. Yeah, she'll be okay.' Because that was what you said, wasn't it? No matter the way the panic was coursing through your body, sending tiny, aggressive bolts of electricity to your nerves, no matter the way your throat was constricting, making it hard to speak at all. When you were trying to reassure each other, that is what you said.

She hung up and fumbled with her phone as she tried to order an Uber. Swore when her fingers were trembling too much to do it, then immediately gave up and tore from the house. It would be quicker to get the Tube. And for the first time in over a year she didn't think of all the ways it could go wrong, leaving the house. Because only one thing mattered. Scarlett. Her best friend, in hospital. Her best friend, needing her.

Chapter Four

He holds my hand the whole time in the ambulance. This man, this stranger, clings to my fingers as if, by doing so, he is anchoring me to life. Maybe he is. Maybe that's why I'm still here, hovering. I wonder if my hand is still warm. I can see it there, limp in his, but I can't feel it. I try to reach out somehow, try to move my fingers, squeeze this man's hand back, but nothing happens. My eyes are closed, even as the paramedics are pumping, trying CPR. My body looks limp, fragile. I suppose it is. Or was. Fragile enough to be switched off, just like that.

The paramedics are still pumping my body, attaching a mask to my face. Do they know that I'm dead yet? Maybe I'm not. Maybe this experience – looking down on myself like this – comes only because I have been knocked out of consciousness. Out-of-body experiences. People have them, right? So maybe that's what this is. It would explain why there is no bright light to go towards, no tunnel. No sign of my grandmother, dead for years now, or some other guide, coming to take me away. I've never given much thought as to what happens after you die, and right now that seems stupid.

I'm oddly calm as I watch, the sirens blaring, the paramedics' words washing over me, like they are unimportant. 'What's her name?' the smaller of the two asks the man.

'I don't...' He swallows, his Adam's apple visibly bobbing. 'Scarlett. Her name's Scarlett.' He knows because he spoke to Evie. I could hear her voice at the other end of my phone when he answered it. Answered it from where it was still in my handbag. Where is my handbag now? I can't see it anywhere in the ambulance, so it must still be there, lying in the middle of the road. The bag I worked so hard for, gone by now, no doubt. Taken by some random passer-by, their lucky day.

Something surges up inside me. It takes me a moment to recognize it as nausea. Which is odd. How can I be nauseous without a body? But I am. And I don't want to be here. I don't want to be looking at myself, don't want to see them fighting to bring me back. Don't want to look at the blood, still trickling from my head, matting in my hair. I don't want to think about Evie, rushing to get to me, when there isn't a *me* to get to. But I'm pulled along with my body, no choice in the matter.

'I'm sorry,' the man is saying now, talking over the paramedics, who are saying my name over and over, telling me to stay with them. The man's face is pale, almost as pale as mine, and his hair is flopping into his eyes. 'I'm sorry.' Again and again. He's gripping my hand so tightly now that it looks like it would be painful. Something twists in me, watching, but it's like a distant echo. My emotions are there, but dim. Like I'm somehow protected from them.

The ambulance pulls up outside the hospital and then it's all action. The paramedics wheeling me out. Doctors, running to meet us. My hand pulled from the man's grip, him following behind, stumbling over his own feet. The doctors asking crisp, efficient questions as they wheel me towards the hospital entrance. Why? Do they think they'll be able to fix me? *Will* they be able to fix me? Fix my body so I can go back to it? Maybe that's why I'm still here, the essence of me – because I've still got a chance. I should feel hopeful at that. Or anxious, maybe. I know I should, but none of the emotions come, everything still on mute. I, who usually feel everything so strongly, so immediately. I've never been the calm, measured one – that's Evie.

The man is told to wait as I'm rushed through double doors, one of my arms falling limply off the trolley. He looks around him, blinking in the harsh hospital lighting. The scrape on his face looks worse under this artificial light. There are people all around, sitting in the waiting area, some of them eyeing the man up, like they are wondering what he's doing here. He just hovers, like he's waiting for some explicit instruction. I hover too, staying this side of the double doors. No one seems to be allowed through there, except for the doctors, and for some reason that seems to include me. Me as in the real me, not my body. And actually I don't want to see them keep pumping at my heart, trying to drag me back from wherever I am now.

A second before the revolving hospital doors start moving, I know. It's like I can feel her energy. Then she comes running through, her dark hair flying, her coat buttoned up all wrong. I can see that ugly cardigan underneath, the one with all the holes. Why does she insist on wearing that? It makes her look frumpy, and she's not. Her green eyes are wide, and she's breathing heavily. Too heavily, really. She stumbles to a stop in the waiting room, eyes darting around frantically, like she's looking for someone. Looking for me. Again I feel that echo of a twist, like a phantom pain.

When she starts moving again, her gait is stiff, awkward. I've got so used to it, it's odd to notice it now. Maybe it's something that's more evident in a hospital, where people are expecting you to be ill or injured.

She crosses to the reception desk. 'I'm looking for my friend.' I can see she's trying to be firm, but the words come out all shaky.

The receptionist looks up, blinks a few times as if trying to draw Evie into focus.

'My friend,' Evie repeats. 'Scarlett Henderson. I'm sure she must be here by now. There was an accident and she…' Her voice seems to be choked away and she takes a steadying breath. 'Where is she now? Please.' The last word comes out as a whimper, and I feel my lack of a body most acutely in that moment. When I can't lay a comforting hand on her shoulder.

'I'll try to find out from the doctors,' the woman says, her voice soft, level. Used to dealing with other people's panic, I'm sure. 'Please take a seat in the meantime.'

I can see the words Evie wants to snap back. Can see the colour rise up her neck as she clamps her lips together.

Of course she can't just *take a seat*. Who does this woman think she is? I would have snapped it out, but Evie only gives her a look, holding it in. The man, who I'd forgotten about, my attention wholly on Evie, comes up behind her.

'Are you Evie?' His voice is hoarse, like he's been shouting.

Evie spins to him. 'Yes. Why? Who are you?'

'I'm Nate.' He winces, like he realizes how insignificant that is. 'I'm the one who… Who was with her.' Was *with* me. It's all wrong, the way he phrases it.

'What happened?' Evie asks quickly. 'Is she okay? Where is she? What happened?' She lurches towards him, takes his hands in hers, the action heartbreakingly vulnerable.

'I… Maybe we should sit down.'

'Will everyone stop telling me to sit down!' She drops his hands, pulls both of hers through her hair. It's still matted from this morning – I bet she hasn't even brushed it. 'It's bad, isn't it? That's why you're saying it. People only say to sit down when it's bad.'

It's true, isn't it? No one ever says, 'Maybe you ought to stand up for this.'

Evie scrunches her eyes closed, then turns, shoulders hunching. She all but collapses onto the nearest chair, one that looks hard and uncompromising.

And in that moment I find myself pulled away. I don't know how or why, but I'm no longer in the hospital, with Evie and Nate. I'm on a beach. I'm laughing, falling down on the sand, with Evie collapsing down next to me, but in joy rather than in defeat. A younger, more carefree Evie.

32

Crete. This is Crete. It's where Evie and I went with a bunch of school friends, after we finished A Levels. We *cannot* stop laughing, I don't remember why. And this is different from the present. I'm not looking down at the scene, I am a part of it. I am in my body – the body I had then. I can feel everything, exactly the way I felt it back then. The sand, sticking to my skin where I've been swimming, the heat of the sun on my face. That feeling of lightness, of the world being *ours*: mine and Evie's. I try to stop laughing, but I can't. I am here, but I am trapped.

'*There* you guys are.' *Now* I stop laughing and look up to see Connor, my first boyfriend. His hands are on his hips as he looks down at Evie and me. God, Connor! I haven't thought about him in years. I think he got married, stayed in our home town, near Cambridge. Maybe he's even got kids by now. I never thought it would last between Connor and me – I was only eighteen, after all, and I was fully aware that he liked me more than I liked him. He was practice, in my head, for when I met the 'real thing'. It seems horribly crass, thinking about it like that now.

'I've been looking for you.' There is a slight accusation in Connor's voice that makes me want to grimace, though the me I'm inhabiting doesn't do that. Instead my body is getting up, moving towards him. Slinking. God, did I really used to slink like that?

'Sorry,' I say, twirling a strand of hair around my finger. Shameless flirt. I suppose that hasn't changed. 'We wanted to enjoy a bit of sun, and you guys were all being lazy.' I smile and I remember that – the way I used to pander to

Connor's insecurities, already aware of how to play the game.

Evie gets to her feet and I can see the self-consciousness returning in the way she crosses her arms across her stomach, over that black swimming costume she's wearing.

'Well, I'm here now,' Connor says. He puts his arms around me, his skin hot against my bare stomach. The smell of his aftershave is too much, like he hasn't yet figured out how much to apply. Did I notice that then? I can't remember. 'Let's go for a swim.' He says the words quietly, and I can tell he's trying to be seductive. Now, in my current consciousness, I want to pull away. I actually strain, trying to reach the edges of my body, trying to make my hands, my feet, listen to *me*. But I don't step away.

'Go,' Evie says with a smile, a casual shake of her hand. 'I'll be fine. I'll head back to the house, I know where it is.' Was I thinking of her then? Or was I only focused on Connor, on making sure that I was playing it exactly right with him? It seems stupid, now, that I was ever worried about that.

'Thanks, Evie.' There's no malice in Connor's voice. He liked Evie. She always knew the right way to play it, to make people like her; when to ask questions, when to laugh. I don't think she knew it – it was something she did subconsciously.

'Have fun!' she says, an edge of a smirk to her smile.

Connor takes my hand, pulls me away from Evie and towards the ocean. I start laughing, squealing as he splashes water up at me. I can feel Evie behind me, but I can't see what she's doing, because the memory-me won't turn to look, turn to see what she's—

Evie. What am I doing, reliving this memory? I don't want to be here, in the ocean with Connor. I need to be with Evie, need to check she's okay, need to—

Just like that, I'm back in the hospital, the memory ripped from me – or me ripped from it – the salt and the sun and the smell of suncream and Connor's aftershave replaced by an odd, weird void. Because I know what hospitals *should* smell like. I can imagine the antiseptic bite, the smell of too many bodies, the tang that we associate with blood. But I can't actually smell it.

Evie is still sitting down on one of the waiting-room chairs. I don't know if the man – Nate – has told her what's happened, but he is perched next to her and she is recoiling from him, shaking her head. So, maybe.

A woman comes out of the double doors, where they had disappeared with my body. A doctor, dressed in scrubs. She scans the room, and I see her clock Nate. Nate, not Evie. She heads to Nate, heads to this stranger, rather than my best friend. Her gait is crisp, efficient. Face carefully neutral, but her mouth a hard line.

'Sir?' Both of them lurch to their feet, and the doctor glances at Evie briefly before returning her attention to Nate. 'You were with the woman who was brought in just now, in the ambulance?'

Nate nods, but Evie starts speaking before he can. 'Scarlett,' she says. 'She's my friend. What's wrong with her? Is she okay? Can I see her?'

The doctor looks between Nate and Evie again and, when Nate nods, settles on Evie. 'I'm so sorry to be the one to tell you this. She's passed away.' Evie stares at her, her body frozen. 'There was nothing we could do,' the doctor continues, talking calmly as Evie begins to tremble. 'She was dead on impact, and the attempts at CPR…' The doctor continues speaking, but the words get lost on their way to me.

The knowledge settles on me. *Dead.* I knew this all along, of course. It's the reason I didn't follow my body through the doors – because I knew what they were doing was pointless. They must have known it too, tried only to make sure they could say they'd done everything possible.

No one is having to tell Evie to sit down now. She collapses, her body crumpling. She's shaking her head. No. She says it over and over again. The doctor is explaining something to her. Head injury. Spinal cord. Medical language I don't want to hear. Because it belongs to my body, not me.

'I'm sorry.' Nate is repeating it, almost in time with Evie's repeated No. Sorry, sorry, sorry.

I have a rush of emotion then. And this time it is not muted. It is hot. Angry. Because he *should* be sorry. He shouldn't have been on his phone. He shouldn't have been riding his bike one-handed. If he had been concentrating, he wouldn't have had the accident, and then I wouldn't have been compelled to go to him, to help him. He'd be on his way to wherever he was going, and I'd be heading to the office. To Jason, to my boss, to the investors.

I stay there, suspended wherever I am, and watch as Evie finally gives herself over to the tears. She shouts at the doctor to leave her, to *do more*, ignoring, or oblivious to, the looks of the other people in the waiting room. Nate reaches out a hand to lay on her arm, then grimaces, seems to think better of it and takes a step back, away from her.

Good. I don't want him near her. If Nate hadn't been so careless, I'd still be here – and she wouldn't *need* comforting. If, if, if. Scenarios flash before me, an amalgamation of images and memories. It's too much. I can't make sense of it. I can't make sense of anything.

Except this. Except for the fact that I would be alive, if it wasn't for this man.

Chapter Five

Evie stood in the corner of the gravel car park, away from the little church in a town on the outskirts of Cambridge, near where she and Scarlett grew up. People were coming out now after the funeral, getting ready to go to the wake, but she didn't want to talk to them. She didn't think she could bear it if someone came up to her to ask her how she was. So instead she was out here, hunched against the grey sky in her coat, waiting for the crowd to thin.

She'd been one of the first ones to flee from the church. Most other people had gone to the front, where Scarlett was lying in her sleek, dark coffin. Mel and Graham had been up there, Graham keeping a supporting hand on Mel's shoulder the whole time. Evie couldn't imagine what it must be like for them. Having to listen to people say again, over and over, how sorry they were. Mel had broken down in the middle of her speech, and Graham had to finish it for her. So no, Evie hadn't wanted to go up to the front to see Scarlett's parents. She'd check on them later, but right now she thought that maybe they, like her, could do with a few seconds of peace. Besides, it wasn't Scarlett, in that coffin. Not really.

Tears burned the back of her eyes and she scrunched them shut, digging her hands further into her coat pockets, trying desperately to keep herself pieced together. When she opened her eyes she saw a man, watching her. As their gazes met, he stepped towards her. His deep-brown eyes were intense and focused on her. It took her a moment to place him. He looked different than he had in the hospital, wearing a black suit, his hair somewhat tamed and without that wild-eyed look. The scrape on his face had healed over, though it had the pink glow of new skin, and his chin was grazed with stubble. Still, she couldn't forget the face of the person who had been with Scarlett when she'd died.

He moved slowly, like he was afraid she might flee at the slightest sound. Little did he know she *couldn't* flee, even if she wanted to. Her muscles were stiffer than usual today. The tightness was keeping her upright, though, locked in place, so maybe she should be grateful for it, because it stopped her collapsing where she stood.

Scarlett had been gone for two weeks now. Two weeks to the day. Evie had taken leave from work temporarily, and the time had felt both impossibly long and like she'd only just blinked since that moment in the hospital. The moment the doctor had said those words. *She's passed away.*

She'd mainly been in her bedroom since then, only venturing further into the flat when she absolutely had to. Apart from her bedroom, everything else in the flat had been Scarlett's too, and Evie could hardly bear it. But if she went to her mum's she'd have to talk, have to reassure her mother, have to listen to complaints about whatever ailment her mum thought she was currently suffering, and she couldn't face it. Better to be alone. She'd taken sleeping pills to get her through. She didn't usually, because if she did, the drowsiness carried over into the next day and she had enough of that without any help. But these two weeks she'd welcomed that feeling of being pulled under, like her head was full of cotton wool, because that sense of surrealness, of not being quite there, was all that was keeping her going.

The man – Nate, she remembered – was now hovering in front of her, shoving his hands into his pockets, maybe against the chill that was lingering in the air, made worse by the wet feel of it, the one that hints at rain. It felt fitting to her that it should rain today, and she welcomed the grey sky above. Because it felt *right* that the very world should mourn Scarlett's absence.

'Hi, Evie.' Nate's voice sounded rusty, too harsh on her fragile nerves. She almost winced at it. He was taller than her, she noted now – a good head above her, which was rare.

'Hello.' The word felt like such an effort to get out.

'How are you doing? Are you okay?'

Evie stared at him, felt her eyelids blink slowly. Even that was an effort. Why was he talking to her? What did he want? She couldn't ask either question out loud. Scarlett would have. She could imagine Scarlett rolling her eyes at her, for holding in what she was really thinking. Just like she'd imagined her grin, fast and wicked, during Evie's funeral speech. *Successful, bright, loving* and *kind, hmm? Stop, Eves, you'll make me blush, all these compliments. What about annoying, overbearing, a little selfish…?* It would have

40

made Evie laugh, and Scarlett would have shaken her head. *It's a lot to live up to, all these adjectives.* Evie almost smiled, actually felt her face soften. Until it hit her, all over again. Scarlett couldn't live up to anything any more.

'Shit, I'm sorry,' Nate said, running a hand through his hair. 'Of course you're not okay. I didn't mean...' He reached out, as if to lay a hand on her arm, then dropped it to his side. He looked across at the church – a grey building against a grey sky – then back at her. 'I hate funerals,' he said on a sigh.

'Been to many, have you?' Her voice was a little cutting. She didn't know what made her say it. Only that her defences were down and she didn't have as much control over herself as she usually did. It was something she was usually proud of: the fact that she, for the most part, could stop herself snapping. She might not have control over her body, but some things she *could* control. Today, though, something in her felt broken.

There was a pause that went on for a beat too long before Nate said, 'One. Other than...' Other than *this* one, is what he didn't say. Still the word 'one', the way he said it, made her heart clench and she felt an echo of guilt wash through her. Only an echo, she didn't have room for more, but still. Because this was her one, wasn't it? It shouldn't be Scarlett, she thought, as bitterness rose up in her. It shouldn't be *Scarlett's* funeral that she had to go through first.

'I'm sorry,' Evie said stiffly, and he immediately shook his head.

41

'No. No, I didn't mean… I just, I know it isn't fun. And I know that sometimes you want to escape from everything.' She frowned up at him – because if he knew that, why had he come over? One edge of his mouth crooked up, ever so slightly. 'I suppose I thought that maybe it would be easier to talk to someone you didn't know,' he said, answering her unasked question. 'That you could be alone with me here too.'

A lump clogged her throat and she looked down at the gravel, her vision blurring with tears. Because that was just it, wasn't it? With Scarlett gone, she *was* alone. She took a breath, felt it hitch, tried to shove down the sob. She'd sobbed solidly for the first few days, had felt them racking through her, tearing her from the inside out until it had felt like there would be nothing left of her. During the funeral she had tried not to cry because she knew that once she did, she wouldn't be able to stop – and she had to give her speech. Scarlett had explicitly told her to, when Evie had broached the subject of funerals. She'd always assumed she'd die before Scarlett. It had seemed obvious, especially after her diagnosis. So it had been Evie obsessing over it, and Scarlett had tried to make it into a fun conversation, getting into the swing of planning her own funeral. *You have to do a speech, even if you don't want to. Obviously my future husband will do one too, and my mum. If she's still alive.* Scarlett had frowned. *Though come to think of it, I'll probably be doing a speech at her funeral instead, won't I? God, that's depressing. Why are you bringing up such a depressing subject?*

I didn't mean— Evie had tried to interject, but Scarlett had flapped a hand at her.

Anyway, it would be good if you could get a celeb there. You know, one of the Hemsworth brothers. Which is the one in The Hunger Games?

Evie tapped her fingers against her knee. *Chris, I think. I'll look him up, give him a call, shall I?*

Yes, exactly. Just to help my future label, you know? So that my creations live on after me. Scarlett threw her head back and gave a proper evil, mwahahaha laugh, lifting her wine in the air, like she was toasting her future success. *And I want that song. You know, the one we always dance to?*

I'm not sure I'd call it a song, it's more—

You have to play it. Scarlett put her wine down and took Evie's hands in hers. *You have to play it, because you'll do it better than a recording, and then it will really mean something, you know?*

I don't think I'll be able to—

Evieeee, Scarlett had said, using that same whiny voice she employed whenever she thought Evie was being annoying or uncooperative. And Evie had laughed, because Evie *always* laughed whenever Scarlett did this.

Fine. I'll play it.

A false promise, one she hadn't fulfilled. Hadn't because she *couldn't*, but still – the one thing her best friend had asked her to do and she hadn't done it. She'd played the song on the speakers instead, connected by Bluetooth to her phone.

Jason had been there, at least. She'd only seen photos of him, but she knew it was him. She hadn't invited him directly, hadn't known how to get in touch, but had sent a message to Scarlett's office and clearly it had reached him. Evie didn't really want him there, but she knew Scarlett would have. She'd nearly gone up to him, nearly put him on the spot. *So, how did you know Scarlett?* she'd ask and watch him turn red. She doubted she'd actually have done it, but she'd never even had the chance. He walked out the moment the ceremony was over – the very first one to leave. Like Scarlett meant nothing to him.

Tears spilled over and she wiped them away, aware of Nate still watching her. 'What are you doing here?' It was an effort to keep her words from slurring. She only got that when she was particularly tired or stressed, but she hated when it happened, the lack of control over her own voice.

He grimaced slightly before straightening his face. 'I just came to… Pay my respects.'

Evie felt a flush of hot anger, coming in to chase away some of the fatigue. They were only in this situation because Scarlett had stopped to help Nate. She wouldn't have been hit by that car, if it wasn't for him. She should blame the driver who hit Scarlett, she knew. She *did* blame that driver, had spent yesterday on the phone to the police, trying to get answers as to who the driver was and what had happened to him or her. But the police hadn't given her anything, had only said they'd *let her know* and they were *looking into it*. Useless, meaningless words. And now *this* man was standing in front her – what, trying to console her? Or trying to make himself feel better? She couldn't help it, she blamed him too.

But there was something she wanted to know, something that kept her there, with him. 'Why was she there?'

Nate frowned. 'Sorry?'

'Why was she there?' Evie repeated. 'That day. In Borough Market. That's where you were, right, when she…'

He swallowed, his Adam's apple bobbing, and nodded. 'Yeah. That's where it happened.' *It happened.* Such a passive way of stating it. It didn't *happen* – Scarlett died. She was killed.

Evie rolled her stiff shoulders. 'I don't understand why she was there.' The words were almost pleading now, the slur that she hated creeping in. 'I don't… She shouldn't have been there. She was going to work, and she doesn't work there. She works in Soho.' And if she'd been in Soho, where she was supposed to be, then she wouldn't have seen Nate fall from his bike. She wouldn't have stopped to help, she wouldn't have…

'I don't know why she was there.' His tone was gentle, less rusty now. 'We barely—' He broke off, shook his head. 'I don't know,' he repeated. 'I'm sorry.'

She closed her eyes. Of course he didn't know. Why would he? The only person who knew was Scarlett.

'I have to go,' she said, her eyes still closed. Though she made no effort to move. People were going to want to talk to her, once she got to the wake. She'd avoided speaking to her old school friends so far, people she and Scarlett hadn't seen in years. They'd all been crying through the service,

45

the girls with mascara stains under their eyes. Evie hadn't even bothered to put mascara on this morning, though she knew Scarlett would have berated her for it. *Don't you want to look your best for me, Eves?*

She shouldn't feel angry at them. She was sure they really *were* sad – just because they weren't a big part of each other's lives any more didn't mean they couldn't feel the loss. But it was bubbling inside her now, this anger, looking for an outlet. She took a breath to try and steady it, felt the cool air linger inside her mouth, like it was trying to soothe her.

'Okay,' Nate said, still in that same gentle tone of voice. She hated it. She didn't *want* gentleness, not from him.

Her eyes snapped open. 'Are you coming to the wake?'

'No,' he said after a beat, and Evie felt relief wash through her. 'I don't want to intrude.'

She nodded. Maybe she should say that he wouldn't be intruding, but he would be, and she didn't want him there. She didn't bother saying goodbye.

'Wait.' She turned back to see him fumbling in his trouser pocket. He produced a business card, handed it to her. She took it automatically, though she frowned at it. 'It's my card,' he explained.

She looked down, read it. 'You're a journalist?' She knew her words sounded flat, void of any genuine interest.

He ran a hand through his hair. 'Yeah. Travel mainly. Though I'm sort of in between jobs at the moment, so I'm in London, for a few weeks.' He shook his head, as if realizing it was irrelevant. 'But look, if you need anything…

I mean, I don't know what you'd need from me, but if you do, then call me. That's my mobile number.'

Evie glanced down at it numbly and then, because she was still *her* enough not to thrust it back at him, she slipped it into her coat pocket. 'Okay,' she said, by way of acknowledgement. When she started walking away this time she felt herself wobble, and even as she gritted her teeth, willing her body to cooperate, she stumbled. Nate was beside her in an instant, crossing the distance in a smooth, even stride that she envied. He put his hand under her elbow to steady her.

She snatched her arm away, glared at him. 'I'm not drunk.' The words were barbed and out, before she could think better of them. It was a sign of how she was feeling, that she'd let it happen twice now.

'I wouldn't judge you if you were,' Nate said evenly.

She didn't know why she felt the need to justify it, to him of all people. She supposed she just hated the idea of him thinking she'd be disrespecting Scarlett like that. 'I have MS,' she said, the words coming out on a sigh. 'Multiple sclerosis.' She looked at him, waiting to gauge his reaction. Waiting for the wince, the grimace, the eyes brimming with sympathy. The wave of a hand in the air, as someone told her they knew so-and-so with it and they were fine. The immediate look to her legs, as other people wondered if she'd be disabled soon but were too polite to ask. Or the frown and *That's a disease, right? But you don't look ill.*

Instead Nate cocked his head. 'Okay.'

She frowned at the complete non-reaction. 'It makes me walk funny sometimes,' she added, almost impatiently.

'Yeah. I don't know much about it, but I've heard it can do that. That sucks – I'm sorry.' He sounded sincere but not overly apologetic, in the way that usually set her teeth grinding. For some reason, that made her feel stupid for bringing it up. Why would he care? Why was she telling him? It was none of his business. So she turned and, holding her head as high as she could, left him standing there. She caught sight of her mum, waiting by the car, ready to drive her to the wake. Saw Scarlett's parents, her dad resting a hand on her mum's shoulder, coming out of the church. *You can do this*, she told herself. She didn't really believe it, but that didn't matter. She only had to get through a couple of hours, and then she could leave and seek comfort in the pills sitting next to her bed.

Chapter Six

I watch as Evie turns her back on Nate, leaves him standing there. Watch Nate watch Evie, and feel a rush of something hot and ugly. He shouldn't be watching her, shouldn't even be *talking* to her.

I'm glad she left him like that. I know exactly how she feels, because I feel the same. I wish I'd never stepped off that damn pavement, never gone to help him. I hate him for it. That's the heat. It can't crawl under my skin, so instead it takes over my sense of self, encompassing me. I hate this man because he is the reason I'm not there, with the people I love, but am rather confined to this limbo. If it weren't for him, I wouldn't have to watch my mum break down, watch my dad try to keep it together, watch Evie lose all the vibrancy she has left. Maybe Nate would have been fine, if I hadn't stopped. Maybe he would have got up, grabbed his bike out of the road without an issue and walked away. Maybe someone else would have stopped. Maybe not – maybe the car would have hit him instead of me – but then I would still be here. There.

There's so much I still want to do. I want to know if it was real, between me and Jason. I want to get married, have the perfect wedding, and ache from smiling so much. I want to see if it would have worked, this new fashion label, and I want to keep trying if it doesn't. I want to see people wearing my clothes on the street, want to hear my name on their lips. I want to have left an imprint on the world. I want to have *mattered*.

I'm not even thirty – it's not *fair* that I'm dead.

I hear the sound of Evie sighing, echoing around my head. *That's the thing, though, isn't it, Scar? Life isn't fair.*

And I am back there, pulled into the memory. Two and a half years ago, standing in the same flat I left for the last time two weeks ago, pacing as Evie sits on the sofa. We'd just got home after the neurologist appointment. We hadn't spoken the whole way back, each of us processing. We hadn't really believed it would be anything serious, I don't think. We'd been chatting about nothing on the way to the appointment – my latest Hinge date, Evie's upcoming mini-break with Will, the fact that Henry, her boss, was driving her mad at work. Because surely there was nothing to worry about. Evie was young and healthy. The GP sending her there was a precaution, that was all.

And now… MS.

It's easier to slip into the memory this time, to be there more wholly. I think it's because I don't resist. I don't want to be in the present, watching my friends and family suffering. I don't want to see the shockwaves I've sent out by dying.

Evie is home now and sitting on our little red sofa. She is still staring straight ahead, as if in shock. It makes sense now. The random tingling pain she sometimes got, something that no painkiller could take away. The attacks of blurred vision, the weird stiffness, the overwhelming tiredness.

It was the tremor that eventually made her go to the doctor. People didn't go to the GP because they felt tired or stiff, did they? Evie had said. Even when the tremor started, it took a degree of nagging on my part to make her go. She didn't want to be a nuisance to the NHS, she said, and I knew she was thinking of her mum. But eventually she'd gone to the GP and had undergone several tests before being referred to a neurologist.

It's far from simple to diagnose, the neurologist had said. *It might have been missed, even if you'd come in earlier.* He'd said it to be kind. That's what I thought: he was trying to be kind, so that Evie didn't blame herself. Because he'd also said that the treatment − only to mitigate, not to cure − was more successful the earlier you caught the disease, and this was not 'early'. *But we've got it now,* he'd said with a bolstering smile and sent us home with several information sheets and a medication to try out, to try to reduce the number and severity of 'relapses'.

I throw my hands in the air, my body controlled by my actions then, my current mind unable to change anything. I am pacing back and forth in our tiny living room, wearing away the second-hand black-and-white rug we found in a charity shop. 'It's not fair, Evie!'

That sigh. She closes her eyes, finally breaking her stare, and rubs her hands across her eyelids. 'That's the thing, though, isn't it, Scar? Life isn't fair.'

'But...' I remember feeling annoyed at that, though it doesn't come now. My actions I cannot change, but my emotions are still my own. I wanted her to rage, thought that was what she *should* be doing – mainly because it's what I would be doing. I wanted her to cry and scream. It comes back to me all so easily and I feel a squirm of guilt. 'You're young and brilliant,' I'm saying now, 'and you don't *deserve* this.'

Evie drops her hands and looks at me. Considering that she is so non-confrontational, she has a very direct stare. 'As opposed to all the other people with MS who do deserve it?'

I make a 'hmph' sound. 'That's not what I'm saying. I just… Why aren't you reacting to this?'

Evie shakes her head, and the action looks tired. 'What do you want me to say?' Her voice is resigned and it makes something in me hurt, having to relive this moment. 'That I wish this hadn't happened? Of course I do. I am terrified, Scar.' Her voice changes then, and I hear the break. Something inside me – the body I have then – cracks too with the sound. 'I am *terrified* of where this might go and how this will impact everything, and I'm so…' She takes a breath. 'I am so fucking angry that it has happened to me.'

I so rarely hear Evie swear that the word sends a jolt through me. I see her eyes flash, know that she is shoving that anger down inside her.

'I hate that it will mean I can't do what I love, that I won't ever be able to, that this.' She waves a hand in the air – 'isn't going away.'

I sink down on the sofa next to her. 'I'm sorry,' I say quietly. 'I'm so sorry. I didn't mean that you have to…' I shake my head. 'You can deal with this however you want

52

to. Obviously. And we'll get through it. Okay? I'll help you. We can get those weighted forks or whatever he was on about.' I feel my lips try for an encouraging smile, but even though there is no mirror in this room, I can tell it falls short.

Evie sighs. 'I don't think this is something weighted forks are going to fix.' She tears up and I put an arm around her. She leans her head on my shoulder, a comforting weight. 'Maybe weighted knives,' she says, her voice a little muffled, and I know she's trying.

'Weighted pans?'

'A weighted remote control.'

'Weighted…' I'm out of things, apparently.

Evie flaps a hand in the air. 'The whole bloody apartment can be weighted, why not?'

There's a moment of quiet between us and then I say, 'You'll be okay, you know.'

'But we *don't* know, do we? The main thing I got from that appointment is that he doesn't know. No one *knows* what it's going to be like.' She squeezes her eyes shut, head still on my shoulder. 'We don't know how it will go, don't know whether it will get worse. Don't know, don't know, don't know.' The words bite out from her, uncharacteristically sharp. I get it. I really do. That unpredictability is one of the worst things for Evie, even now. 'If someone could just tell me what was going to happen, then at least I could be prepared.'

I don't say anything to that. This has got to be one of the only times when I don't know what to say to Evie. I can't reassure her that things won't get worse. Because I know they *will* get worse.

Evie opens her eyes. 'I should call Will.' She says it numbly, like it's an obligation, and I make a disapproving 'hmm' noise in the back of my throat. Evie sighs. 'Don't.'

'I didn't say anything,' I say, and my voice sounds a touch defensive.

'No, but I can hear it in your thoughts.'

'Telepathic, are you?'

The ghost of a smile flitters across her lips. 'Only with you.'

I scoff. 'Boring. I'd rather have the ability to fly.'

I get a laugh then, and something in me lightens. 'Or turn invisible?' she suggests.

'Nah, I want people to see me, to know I'm the one doing things. Move at the speed of light – I'd quite like that. No more wasting time getting from A to B.'

'Okay. I'll be the Invisible Woman in *Fantastic Four*, and you can be… Who runs really fast? It's Flash, right?'

I nod. 'Sold.'

Evie's smile stays there for a moment longer before it drops. 'What am I going to tell Will? I don't want… What if he looks at me differently, once I tell him I have this… this *disease*.'

'Well, I know, and *I'm* not looking at you any differently.'

'Yes, but you're *you*.'

I pause, and I know that I was weighing up my words. 'I would wait and tell him when you're ready. *You* haven't even had time to process it yet, so maybe take a few days –

54

or weeks – to figure out how to deal with it yourself first.'

'I can't lie to him.'

'You're not lying. You're just… waiting.'

Evie wrinkles her nose and I can tell she doesn't like that. I value her honesty – really, I do – but she is sometimes quite black-and-white about these things. It wouldn't hurt, would it, not to tell Will immediately?

She tells him a few days later, as far as I remember, and it all goes downhill from there. Not that she should have been with him in the first place. I don't even know why she liked him – or even if she did like him, rather than had got used to him. *He's dependable*, Evie had said, when I asked her about it once. I'd made a face. *Maybe* you *should be looking for a bit more dependable in your life*, she'd shot back.

I'd scoffed. *Nah. Not really my style, Eves.*

'It'll be okay,' I repeat and Evie nods. She doesn't look convinced, though, so I keep going. 'We'll get through it, Eves. We'll take it as it comes and figure it out, all right?'

She sighs. 'You know I love you, right? In case I forget to say it in the future when my brain goes all funky, or if my speech goes funny and I can't get the words out.' Although there's real worry hidden under her tone, I laugh, because she's trying to joke.

'I'll remind you of that when you complain about my washing-up skills or my terrible drunken behaviour at parties.' She smiles a little. After a pause I say, 'You know I love you too?' Why has it always been so easy, to say it to Evie? I suppose it's a different kind of love – one that's easier to be sure of than The Love.

'Thanks, Scar,' Evie says in the memory. 'Thanks for coming with me.'

'Always.' Then I clap my hands. 'Right.' She sits up properly and I slip out my phone, connect it to our Bluetooth speaker. Then I give her a look. 'You know what this calls for…'

She makes a face, shakes her head. But I ignore her. Press Play. And there it is: our song. Because, fine, it doesn't have any words and Evie is picky about that, but what else are you supposed to call it? It's the music that they played at my funeral – the song I'd asked Evie to play, but she didn't. Because of the tremor, I know. I can't even remember when it started – we were teenagers, I think, and it came on Spotify, and it's so *joyful* that we just decided. This is ours.

I turn the volume up, get to my feet and hold out a hand. 'You know the rule,' I say firmly. The rule that whenever either of us hears this song, no matter where we are or who we are with, we have to dance. We have to dance *ridiculously* – as ridiculously as we can. Which works out well, because neither of us has any dancing skills to speak of.

Evie makes another face, and for a moment I think she's going to refuse. But she doesn't – she gets up. How could I have forgotten that? She *gets up*. And we are dancing, the two of us, and we are fucking ridiculous, sashaying around the sofa, and Evie does a move where she goes all stiff and then moves side-to-side, making fun of her own diagnosis, and it makes me laugh so hard that I snort.

I'd *forgotten* this. I remember her getting her diagnosis, but I'd forgotten that she'd managed to get up and dance with me afterwards. It wasn't an immediate switch being flipped in her, but more of a gradual wearing down, things eroding her self-confidence more and more as she started to let the illness define her.

When was the last time we danced like this? I can't remember – I think I stopped trying, assuming she'd refuse, and now I'll never have the chance again. And Evie, will Evie dance like this again, I wonder? Will she dance again at all?

Chapter Seven

Evie lay on the sofa with headphones in her ears. There was no real reason for the headphones any more, she supposed. No one else in the flat to hear the music, to look at her with sympathy at the fact that she listened to the type of music she could no longer play. But it was a habit. She was listening to a piece of music that was supposed to be soothing, though the tiredness she felt made it difficult to know whether she felt *soothed* or just exhausted. It wasn't that bone-deep MS fatigue that hit her suddenly, at random parts of the day. This was more an ordinary tiredness. She'd slightly lost track of what ordinary was at this stage, but her symptoms hadn't been as bad over the last couple of weeks and she'd weaned herself off the sleeping pills, knowing the reliance on them would only make her problems worse in the long run.

It was Friday, and after the weekend she had to go back to work. Even the four weeks she'd taken had been pushing it. The HR manager was generally really nice, as well as being super-professional, but there was only so much she could do. *It wasn't a close family member, Evie.* She hated that. Hated having to try and qualify her relationship with Scarlett. Still, it might be good for her, she'd acknowledged in a detached sort of way, to go back to work. A reason to get up in the morning. She'd have to make an effort to go back into the office after this, too – Henry wasn't going to want her working from home after such a long break.

She roused herself enough to pick up her phone where it lay on the sofa next to her. She had a text message from her mum – she resolutely refused to get WhatsApp – asking her to call her back. She'd been ignoring her mother's calls and she did the same thing now, telling herself she'd reply by the end of the day. Alongside the message there was a missed call. She sat upright, reading the number. It could be the police calling her back, finally. But it was a mobile number. Would the police be calling her from a mobile number? She googled it on her phone, but it came up with no matching results. And there was no voicemail. Surely if it was important they'd leave a voicemail?

She put her phone down, glanced around the flat. It was too bare. She'd packed away Scarlett's things last week, unable to keep looking at them. Not her bedroom – she hadn't been able to bring herself to go in there. She'd opened the door and looked in, but her feet had stopped at the threshold. The curtains had been open and the room had seemed too bright, when it should be in mourning. She'd wanted to snap at the room, *Show some respect!* But, of course, it was a room and even if it wanted to, it couldn't close its own curtains.

Scarlett always slept with the curtains open. It was something that had always baffled Evie, but Scarlett said that she liked knowing when the world was awake, so she could wake up with it. She'd envied Scarlett's endless energy, especially in recent years, when it felt like she had none of her own. Now she only missed it.

She'd asked Scarlett's parents to come and pick her things up, clear out her room, but Mel had said she couldn't face it, and Evie didn't want to be the one to do it, so that was that. She felt a pang. She'd always been close to Mel and Graham, Mel especially, but she'd barely spoken to them since the funeral.

There was a knock at the door. Evie stayed sitting for a moment, hoping it would go away. But the knock sounded again, and she resigned herself to getting up. Her body felt slightly easier to move today, a relief after the tightness that hounded her.

She opened the door and stared.

'Will.' She said his name out loud, her eyebrows pulling together.

'Hello, Evie.' His voice was as slick and smooth as she remembered. He was clean-shaven, as always, his dark-blond hair flopping into his eyes. Broad-shouldered and muscled, from all that time he spent in the gym.

Something tightened in her gut as she scanned his face, taking in the familiar contours, but she wasn't sure what it was. When did she last see him? Around eight months ago, she thought, when they'd exchanged boxes of each other's things. But the last real conversation they'd had was before that, when he'd told her he was sleeping with someone else, over morning coffee in the flat one weekend, when Scarlett hadn't come home from the night before.

'Someone let me in downstairs,' Will said, a subtle shift in his body the only sign that he was at all anxious about showing up on her doorstep. But then he'd always been the overly confident type – it was part of what had made things easy between them, because it allowed her to follow his lead. Evie frowned, and Will lurched on with an explanation before she could say anything. 'I heard about Scarlett and I wanted to come and see if you were okay.' He gave her a small smile. 'I thought you could do with a friend.'

She considered him for a moment. Really she should slam the door in his face, shouldn't she? Her fingers twitched, like she might actually do it. What would she say? *Fuck you?* That was pretty dramatic, right?

She dropped her hand from the door, stepped aside to let him in. Because she'd never quite been able to master the *fuck-you* attitude that had come so naturally to Scarlett. And because… Fine, because she *did* need a friend and, well, beggars couldn't be choosers, could they?

When did you get so pathetic, Evie?

She decided it was best not to answer that.

'Do you want a tea?' She was a little taken aback by how hoarse her voice was. When was the last time she'd spoken to someone out loud?

'I'll make it,' Will said quickly, shrugging out of his leather jacket and hanging it up on the back of the door before heading for the kitchen. 'I remember where everything is.'

Evie followed him with her gaze. He looked so natural in her kitchen, like they'd slipped back in time. She couldn't think of anything to say, so she said nothing, just watched. She clocked the brochures, still sitting on top of the microwave – the ones Scarlett had brought home, the night before she died. Her last night with Scarlett, and they'd spent it arguing.

She crossed onto the plasticky floor of the kitchen, tried to be subtle as she moved aside for Will to get to the kettle and slipped the brochures off the microwave, shoving them in a drawer instead. No need for Will to see them.

What was he doing here? Did he really want to see how she was? They hadn't spoken since they'd broken up. He'd made it all sound so reasonable. She was always so tired, never wanted to do anything, wasn't taking an interest in his life, his hobbies. His hobbies, which mainly consisted of going to the gym or *being* at the gym in some respect, and which she couldn't have joined in with, even if she'd wanted to. And then the crunch point. *It's like you never want to have sex any more.* And yes, coming to terms with an incurable disease had sort of affected her libido, and the fatigue that hit her hard some days made that even worse. Not that she and Will had ever had the most passionate relationship – it was more a sort of routine, she'd thought – but towards the end their sex life had been almost non-existent. It's what he'd thrown at her, when he'd told her he was cheating on her.

What, so this is my fault?

No! No, no, that's not what I meant. I'm just trying to explain. She'd sat completely still, not knowing how to process it. He'd cleared his throat. *Maybe I should leave.*

She'd bitten down the million things she wanted to scream at him, the names she wanted to call him. Bitten down the churning inside her as she said, *Yes, I think that's best.*

They hadn't even officially had the 'break-up talk'. She'd waited for him to call, to beg and, when he didn't, well, that was that. It was Scarlett who'd had to deal with the aftermath and the spiral that it sent Evie into, because it was *proof*, wasn't it, that there was something wrong with her? Proof that no one would want to be with her – because it meant being with her MS too.

But now Will was here. Back. Because he regretted it? Because he genuinely wanted to be her friend?

He handed her a mug of tea and there was something comforting in it, in being taken care of. After weeks on her own, someone was here, looking after her.

They stood on opposite sides of the small kitchen counter, and Will rested his elbows on the surface. His grey-blue eyes – less vibrant than Scarlett's blue – scanned her face, like he was looking for physical signs of damage.

'So, how are you?' he asked, and his voice was so smooth, so confident. Like he didn't see any reason why they *wouldn't* be here, having this conversation.

'I'm…' Evie lifted her tea, cupping the mug in both hands, seeping some of its comforting warmth. 'God, I don't know. I'm coping, I guess.' She wasn't sure if it was true. She wasn't sure whether other people would agree with her definition of 'coping'.

'She was an amazing person,' Will said, though it sounded off, coming from him. They hadn't really liked each other, Will and Scarlett, and neither had made much secret of the fact. 'It's shocking,' he carried on, 'to think about it.'

Evie nodded, because what else could she do? It was a stupid thing to say. The *wrong* thing to say. Though if someone asked her what the right thing was, she wouldn't be able to tell them.

'So let's not,' Will said, straightening off the counter.

'What?'

'Let's talk about something else, shall we? A distraction? How's work?'

'Oh, don't ask me about that,' Evie said with a tired wave of her hand. He continued to look at her, eyes probing. 'Henry is still a nightmare, let's put it that way.' He'd already texted her, when he'd found out that she was coming back on Monday, saying that they needed to 'talk' about his anniversary. Because of course he couldn't figure out what to do on his own. And really, weren't advertising people supposed to be creative?

'Still making you buy his wife and daughter birthday presents?'

She tried for a smile, though the effort almost felt painful. 'Every year without fail.' She didn't tell him that she'd been on bereavement leave – it felt like a weakness. 'But let's not talk about me. How's your work going?'

Will smiled, his perfect white teeth flashing. She knew he'd paid to have them whitened. Was that, like, an annual thing or did you only do it once? Presumably they didn't *stay* that bright white unless you kept doing it? 'Good. I got a promotion.'

'Really?' She could hear how hollow her voice sounded and tried to inject some life into it. 'That's great.' He'd been working towards it before they'd broken up. She wasn't actually sure how a promotion in estate agenting would mean something different, other than the obvious more money, but she knew it was important to him. Selling better houses? she supposed. The bigger, more expensive ones? She'd made fun of him once, when she'd overheard him on the phone, trying to upsell a one-bed flat in Hackney: *Perfectly compact, easy to manage when you've got a busy lifestyle – save money on those cleaner fees, eh?*

So basically you're saying it's about big enough to fit one single bed in, and you should only move in if you're too poor to afford a cleaner?

Will hadn't got it.

She let him talk, his voice washing over her, and was grateful for the fact that he seemed to need minimal input from her, just the occasional nod or 'Uh-huh'. He was right, though, to some degree. It was a distraction from the abyss that was waiting for her.

He made another round of teas and they moved over to the sofa. So familiar, this routine. There was some comfort in the predictability of it all.

'Shall we put on a film?' Will asked, picking up the control from where it sat on the coffee table and flicking through Netflix. 'Let's go action,' he said decisively. 'Nothing too sad or mushy.'

Evie made a sort of nod-shrug action, knowing full well she'd switch it off when he left. Which would be when, exactly? she wondered. She studied him while his attention was on the TV. 'Will, why are you here?'

He looked over at her. 'I told you, I thought you could do with a friend right now.' His voice seemed genuine enough, but the words felt sticky in her mind. Were they ever really friends? She supposed so, inasmuch as people who were in a relationship usually had a degree of friendship. But they'd met on a dating app, and they'd never been true friends before they started sleeping together – and they certainly hadn't been friends after they'd broken up. But maybe it would be nice to have someone around that she knew. London already felt so lonely without Scarlett.

He put on some movie, she didn't even look at the title, then set the remote down and turned to her. 'Also… I missed you, Evie.' She could only frown. It was the first she was hearing of it. 'I've wanted to get in touch for months now, but I wasn't sure how to. And then I heard the news and I… well, I suppose it gave me the push I needed.' There was something uncomfortable in there, the fact that it took Scarlett's death for him to get in touch, but Evie stopped her brain from going too far down that route, knowing it would only make her feel worse.

He reached out, trailed a hand down her arm, and she couldn't help leaning towards him. She wanted that connection. For someone to hold her, tell her it would be okay. No one had done that. Her mother wasn't the type to, and Scarlett's parents were dealing with their own grief. Her school friends had offered brief hugs, but no one had really *held* her. She was surprised by how much she craved it.

He moved in closer and she knew what would happen. Will's moves were always the same. He cupped her neck, stroked his thumb down her jawline. She just looked at him, neither moving towards him nor pulling away. He leaned in, kissed her neck, then her lips – all so comfortingly predictable. She felt her body respond automatically, remembering the dance. And why shouldn't she? She didn't want to be alone, didn't want to be lonely.

She'd thought he was seeing someone. Not the same girl he'd been cheating on her with, but she'd seen photos of him and a new girlfriend on Instagram. Maybe it hadn't been a girlfriend after all. Or maybe they'd broken up in the last month. She'd stopped going on social media now, because a lot of her friends were posting about Scarlett, pinning photos of her, saying how sorry they were, and Evie couldn't stand it. It might have stopped by now, but she couldn't be sure. What was the point of it all? Scarlett wasn't there to see any of it.

Though if she *were* able to see it, the chances were that she'd love all the social posts. The way people were celebrating her, mourning her. She loved being the centre of attention, after all. It almost made Evie smile, and Will misread her expression.

'There you are,' he said softly and leaned in to kiss her again. She returned it, let him lay her back on the sofa, moving to brace himself above her. Let him, because it was easier than resisting and because, yes, she did want a distraction, and because she missed it, that physical affection, at a time when she felt impossibly lonely. Because Scarlett was gone, her essence dissipated the moment the car hit her, and she'd rather be kissing Will than thinking about that. So she let him pull off her shirt, then ran a hand up his muscled chest when he stripped down himself, the steps easy because she'd done them so many times before.

She didn't think about what would be waiting for her once this was over. She only closed her eyes and let her mind go blissfully blank.

Chapter Eight

I don't watch, obviously. Once it became clear where this was heading, I found I could just *not* be there. I can let my mind wander, it seems, and go wherever I choose – past or present. But I had to come back, check up on her. They are dressed now, the two of them, and Evie is sitting up on the sofa, hugging her arms around her.

Will is such a dick. More than that. He's evil. He was so clearly taking advantage of her. I shouldn't be surprised, given the way he was merrily cheating on her, but still, I didn't think he'd stoop so low.

He looks awkward now, fumbling with his clothes, not quite looking at Evie. What the hell did she ever see in him? I mean, I do understand it, the need for affection. And I'm hardly one to talk – I've never gone more than a few months without seeing someone, in some capacity. So it's not like I'm judging Evie for having sex – far from it. If it helps, if it's comforting, then why the hell not? But she is not looking comforted, and this was not her idea – it was his.

I strain desperately to be a physical presence, wanting to shove Will out of the door, make something fly into him. Make him suffer, in some way, for the inevitable pain my friend will be feeling as a result of this.

But no objects fly around the room; neither of them shivers or looks round as if they have felt my presence. There is nothing. I am confined to empty space, my soul lost in a vacuum between life and death.

Will clears his throat. 'I better go.'

Evie gets up, but keeps her arms wrapped around herself. 'I'll walk you out.' She's going vacant again. I hate the idea that she's already regretting this and that when Will goes, it will be even harder for her to keep it together.

They walk down to the ground floor, neither of them making a move to touch the other. Evie opens the door for Will, even though he can do it himself. I suppose she's trying to be polite, walking him out. I would have shoved him out of the flat and been done with it – but then I doubt I'd ever have gone there in the first place with someone like Will. He so obviously has no moral compass.

Then again, am I really one to judge, as far as moral compasses go?

'It was good to see you, Evie,' Will says, leaning over to give her a kiss on the cheek. Did he come here with this explicit goal in mind? I wouldn't put it past him.

'You too,' Evie says, though I can tell the words are automatic, that she doesn't really mean them. I wonder if Will can tell too. I hope so.

She shuts the door after him, then looks down to the pile of letters inside the entrance hall. The postman has an access code and is supposed to deliver the post to each flat individually, but sometimes this happens and we get a

70

bunch of letters lying on the floor in the little entrance hall. She picks up the ones addressed to our flat after a cursory glance at them. One of them is addressed to me.

She's blinking back tears as she heads up the stairs. I wish I knew what she's thinking. It's unfair – shouldn't being dead make you omniscient or something? Shouldn't there be some kind of perk, like mind-reading?

I realize, then. Will didn't once ask how Evie was, healthwise. The thing he blamed the break-up on, the reason he gave for cheating on her, so that it made her think she was unlovable or that she'd be lucky ever to find someone who might 'take her on', and he hadn't even acknowledged it.

Evie jerks to a stop on the stairs. I hear it too. Someone is playing the violin. A little awkward, a little clumsy. Nothing like the way Evie used to play. But it's there.

She keeps going up the stairs, tentatively now. She rounds the corner and stops. There is a girl there, sitting at the top of this flight of stairs, on my and Evie's floor. She is young, early teens maybe. Her mousy brown hair is tied up in a knot on top of her head, and her face is completely clear of make-up. She's wearing baggy trousers and a hoodie and is currently scowling down at her violin.

Evie takes another step and the girl looks up. 'Oh. Hello.'

'Hello,' Evie says slowly, and I can tell she's wondering, as I am, who the hell this girl is.

'Was that guy your boyfriend?' the girl asks and, in all fairness, a part of me appreciates her directness.

'Er…'

71

'I've just moved into the flat opposite you,' the girl says, as if that explains the question. She points to the white door. Number six, opposite our number four. 'Well, I suppose it depends what you mean by *just*. But, like, three days ago.'

'Ah,' Evie says. 'Well then, welcome, I guess.'

'I saw him. Both of you. Walking down. Is he your boyfriend?'

Evie sighs, massaging her temples. 'No.'

'Oh. Is he your friend?'

'Not really.'

'Why did he come over?'

Evie raises her eyebrows, but the girl doesn't retract her question. 'To see if I was okay.'

'Why did he leave?'

'Because he's a man,' Evie says, a little drily.

The girl purses her lips, as if thinking about that. 'I don't think all men leave when you're not okay. That would be really depressing.'

Evie cocks her head. 'Who said I'm not okay?'

'You did. Sort of. You *inferred* it.' She says the word like she's trying it out.

Evie sidesteps this by nodding at the violin. 'You play?'

'Well, I'm trying.' She makes a face. 'It's difficult.'

A small smile pulls at Evie's lips, making me realize that I don't think I've seen her smile at all in the last few weeks. 'Yeah. It is. It's worth it, though.'

The girl nods slowly, twirling her bow between the thumb and forefinger of her left hand. 'You play then?'

72

Evie pales, ever so slightly. 'I—'

But this girl doesn't let Evie finish. 'Mum gets fed up of listening to me in the flat. But I need to practise.'

'So you came into the corridor,' Evie states, and the girl smiles up at her, as if she and Evie are now on the same wavelength.

'Yeah.' She picks up her violin again, places it under her chin the way I've seen Evie do countless times and lifts her bow. She makes a face at the note that comes out, though I don't totally know why.

Evie sits down next to the girl and holds out a hand. 'Can I see?' The girl hesitates, fingers tightening briefly on the violin. 'I'll be careful with it, I promise.' Something about her tone must convince the girl, because she hands it over. Evie takes it gently.

'The tuning is a little out, that's all,' Evie says.

'I had it tuned.'

'Mmm, but if you drop it or something, that can change.' Evie is examining the violin now.

'I'd never drop it.'

Evie lifts her gaze to look directly at the girl. She smiles and it's a genuine, proper smile. 'Good. You shouldn't, not if you care about it. But maybe in the move it got clunked?'

The girl purses her lips again, but says nothing. Evie reaches up, twists one of the knobs a bit. Pegs, I remember. She called them pegs. Her hand trembles as she does so and she scowls.

'What's wrong with your hand?' The girl has sharp eyes – the tremor is subtle today. It only happens when Evie tries

73

to do something. An *intention* tremor, the doctor called it on one of the appointments. Evie takes her hand away from the violin, flexes her fingers, stares at them.

'I have MS.'

'Oh.' The girl wrinkles her nose. 'I think my granny has that. It's where you get tired all the time, right?'

'Sort of.'

'That sucks.'

'Yeah.' Evie is still looking at her hand, almost accusingly, like she's not sure how *this* hand belongs to her.

There's a beat, then the girl says, 'My dad left us. Me and Mum. It's why we're here, because we couldn't afford to stay in the house, but Mum needs to be in London for work.'

Evie lowers her hand. 'I'm sorry. That sucks too.' And she'd know, wouldn't she?

'Yeah.'

Evie pushes through, adjusts the pegs, despite the tremor. She runs one finger down the side of the violin as she finishes. 'Does that feel better?' she murmurs. The girl frowns at her and Evie flushes, like she realizes she's spoken out loud. It is so brilliantly *Evie* that it makes me feel a shade lighter. She does this – talks to violins. Mainly *her* violin, but still.

She clears her throat as she hands the violin back to the girl, as if that will cover it up. 'Here, try that.' The girl does, and it's better, even to my non-discerning ear. Evie stands, ready to leave, but looks down at the girl before she does. 'I'm Evie.'

The girl hesitates. 'Astrid,' she says eventually. Then Astrid goes back to her violin, and Evie leaves her to go inside.

She's still holding the letter as she lets herself into the flat, the one addressed to me. She stares at it – at my name – for a good minute before she sets it down on the kitchen counter, leaving it there unopened. She won't want to open anything addressed to me, I know. And that works out well on this occasion, because I don't want her to open that letter. Because I think I know who it is from, and without me there to explain it all, I know Evie is bound to take it the wrong way. So it's better, all things considered, that she never knows.

Chapter Nine

Evie clocked Nate the moment she stepped inside the café. She hesitated in the doorway, the sound of chatter, mixed with the whirring of the coffee machine and screaming from a toddler in the corner, momentarily overbearing after so long in the silence of her own flat. The heat of the place washed over her, making her too warm in the jacket she'd worn – because you never knew in May, did you?

She slipped her headphones off, then wove through the tables to get to him. He jumped up as he saw her, his gaze flicking over her face as she grew closer. Eyes like coffee, she thought.

'Evie, hi.' His voice was overly formal. He immediately gave a little head-shake, like he regretted the words. 'Can I get you a drink?' Nate plugged on. 'Coffee? Tea?'

'I can get it.' Evie looked over at the counter, where there was a perpetual queue. It was one of the trendy Clapham cafés – a little independent that served poached eggs and avocado on toast and vegan keto brownies, with an array of dairy-free milk alternatives. Scarlett had loved this café, and now that Evie was here, the pit inside her from missing Scarlett was deepening again. She should have suggested somewhere else. But she'd panicked, a bit, when she'd rung Nate, using the number from his business card, and so had said the first place that had come to mind.

'No, no, I'll get it,' Nate insisted, already edging away to the counter. Evie hesitated. But it would be good to sit – she was already feeling tired from the walk there. And she needed a moment to compose herself, to make sure she knew exactly what to say. 'A latte. If you don't mind.'

'One latte, coming up,' he said, lifting a finger in the air. He grimaced again. He was nervous, she realized. Was that a bad sign? Probably, but maybe it would work in her favour – maybe he'd be more likely to tell her what she wanted to know.

She slipped off her jacket as she sat down, swore that she could feel eyes on her from the other customers. *Stop being stupid, Evie*, she told herself firmly. *No one is watching you.* It was a low-level anxiety that had been starting to come on in the months before Scarlett died – the idea that people were watching her, judging her, thinking she looked somehow *different* because of her MS.

She checked her phone as she waited for Nate, partly to distract herself from the squirming in her stomach, the way her palms felt hot and clammy. The music she'd been listening to on the way here – a loud, vibrant piece with strong crescendos and quick builds, something to distract her, to block out everything else – was still playing into her headphones, now tucked into her bag. She closed Spotify, then saw she had two messages. She opened the one from her mum first.

How are you doing? I was going to say you
should come up to Cambridge this weekend,
but I've been feeling a bit under the weather
and I saw an article the other day about avian
flu and I wouldn't want to give it to you, if that's
what I have. I'll go to the doctor on Monday and
will let you know what they say. Maybe we could
meet up if they give me the all-clear?

Evie felt the telltale pulse in her temples, one that flared
whenever she got a message like this from her mum, and
decided to wait before replying.

There was a message from Scarlett's mum too.

That's okay, Evie love. We are carrying on. Stay
in touch and come round soon. Xxx

Her stomach twisted even more. She'd asked Mel how
she was doing, feeling guilty for not doing more for them.
She hadn't told them about her calls to the police yet, not
wishing to make things worse if she didn't get the answers
she wanted.

She put her phone to one side, screen down, as Nate
came back with her latte and a black coffee for himself.
Like Scarlett used to drink. He cleared his throat as he sat.
He still had stubble across his jaw, she noticed – like at the
funeral. So maybe it was a permanent fixture.

'You live around here then?' he asked, batting for an
introduction to the conversation.

'Yeah. Near Clapham North station, if you know it.'

'Sort of. I grew up Kent way, but my brother lives in London now, so I visit him a bit. He's West London, though. Near Hammersmith.'

Evie nodded, pulled her latte towards her. They'd done a leaf, on the top. She'd always admired anyone who could do that sort of thing – transform a coffee into a mini work of art. It made her feel guilty for drinking it. She'd waited once, when she'd been here before. Waited for the leaf to dissipate of its own accord, fading into the froth beneath, before she'd drunk it. Scarlett had laughed at her for being so sentimental.

She clocked Nate watching her and cleared her throat. 'You don't live in London then?'

'No. I don't really live *anywhere*, to be honest.'

Evie frowned in question. *Be polite*, she told herself.

'I move around a lot,' he explained. 'Depending on where my job takes me.'

'Right. Travel journalism,' she remembered.

'Yeah, and other bits. Whatever I can get, really. But I move wherever the piece suits, stay there for a bit, move on when it's done or when I have somewhere else to be.'

'Sounds… interesting.' *Exhausting* was more the word she had in mind, but she felt it would be the wrong thing to say. Because you were supposed to find the idea of travelling alluring, weren't you? But the thought of constantly picking herself up, moving from place to place, felt exhausting – there was no other word for it. 'But you're in London now?' A redundant question.

What she was really thinking was: *why?* If he travelled so much, if he didn't really *live* in London, then why had he been there, the day Scarlett died? Everything could have been different, if he'd not been here.

'Yeah. I came back to visit because I'm in between jobs. And it's my brother's fortieth soon, so I'm going to stick around for that.'

She nodded and found she'd run out of small talk. He seemed to sense that and leaned forward to put his coffee down on the low table between their two armchairs. 'So. You had some questions?'

No point in dancing round it, was there? She sat up a little straighter. 'You told the police it was an accident,' she stated, and he frowned, the expression crossing his face slowly, a gradual slide. Like he was thinking about it. 'I've been calling them,' she explained. When she found herself twisting her hands in her lap, she pulled them apart. 'Trying to find out what they're doing, about Scarlett's death.'

Nate nodded slowly, picking up his coffee but not drinking it. 'It was. An accident, I mean.'

'It wasn't,' Evie countered immediately, then pushed back her hair. 'I mean, it can't have been.' Her voice was imploring. 'That driver, whoever it was' – the police had refused to give Evie a name – 'hit Scarlett. They *hit* her.' Not just hit her, Evie thought, but slammed into her so hard that she'd died, then and there.

When Nate spoke, it was like he was choosing his words carefully. 'She was in the road.'

'She wouldn't have just *been* in the middle of the road,' Evie snapped, feeling her body strum with tension. She took a breath, fought to push it down. These days she always seemed so much closer to simmering point. 'She wouldn't have stood in oncoming traffic. The driver must have been coming too fast, or not been looking or…' But she couldn't finish, her throat closing around the words.

Nate put his coffee down. 'She was getting my bike, from the road.'

'Your bike?' He'd told her that he'd been with her. That he'd fallen from his bike, Scarlett had stopped to help him and that was when she'd been hit. He'd explained all this at the hospital, but she hadn't been in any state to concentrate and she'd come away with the bare minimum.

'My bike, well, my brother's bike' – another head-shake – 'it was in the road and she turned to get it, stepped into the road and…' He let a breath out on a whoosh. 'The car – the driver – didn't have the chance to stop or even to see her, really, or…'

Evie realized she was shaking her head before he'd even finished. But it was wrong. What he was saying was all wrong. 'Scarlett wouldn't *do* that,' she said. 'She wasn't some… She wasn't an idiot – she wouldn't have darted out into moving traffic to get *your* bike, someone she'd never met.' Tears sprang to her eyes and she looked away to hide them. Nate didn't get it. Scarlett was clever. She had her wits about her. She knew exactly when to jump on the Tube as the doors were closing – always timing it exactly right – and she could weave around people on escalators like a ninja and… 'Why are you saying this?' Evie whispered, still not looking at him. 'This person *hit* her, killed her, and because of what you said, the police are…' She turned back to face him. 'They're doing nothing,' she said harshly. 'So no one will pay for what happened.' She swallowed. 'The driver must have run a red light, or been looking at their phone or something.'

'I don't—'

'And how would you even know!' She erupted then, the anger hitting her hot and hard, refusing to be kept in her depths, where it usually hid. And it felt *good* to give into it. To feel something that strongly, after weeks of feeling empty. So she didn't care that everyone really *was* looking at her now. She didn't care what Nate thought of her, whether this would make things worse. She didn't give a damn. 'You had just fallen off your bike, hadn't you? Weren't you on the ground? Could you even *see* the driver coming? How do you *know* that they weren't to blame?'

He grimaced, but said nothing. And she knew: he wasn't going to take it back. This conversation, it had been for nothing. 'There were other people who said the same as me,' he said quietly. 'Other witnesses. And there were cameras, at the lights. If there was any fault then—'

But Evie cut him off with a sharp shake of her head. She didn't want to hear his attempt at a rational explanation. Because nothing about this was *justifiable*. And now he – the key witness, the person Scarlett stopped to help – would not help *her*.

She got to her feet, leaving her latte untouched, the leaf dissipating, and grabbed her jacket. 'This was a mistake,' she said, turning to go.

'Evie, wait.' She took a couple of clumsy steps away from the table, even as she saw him getting to his feet behind her. 'Evie!'

But she had her stride now, and she didn't turn back. She swiped at the hot tears that had spilled onto her cheeks without her noticing. *Useless!* She felt totally and completely useless.

But the anger was still there too. And it was that she held on to as she left. Where usually she'd try to swallow it down, this time she clung to it. Because it was so much easier to have someone to hate, someone to blame, than it was to feel like it was the universe itself that had snatched Scarlett away from her.

Chapter Ten

I feel a vindictive pleasure, seeing Evie storming out, away from Nate. For the second time, I might add.

I'm only realizing now that the driver hasn't featured much in my thoughts. It's been the car, the thing itself, that has made its presence known – and Nate, of course. Seeing Nate's face, in the moment before it hit me. Even now the driver is faceless. I never saw him or her. And I find that I don't want them to have a face, because that will make it feel real. That sounds ridiculous, doesn't it? I know it sounds ridiculous. I know I'm dead, but this in between… I don't know. It's almost like I can pretend it's only temporary, that there will somehow be a way back from it.

I get why Evie wants to see someone punished, though. Only I don't know what she'd do if she found this person, saw them locked up for it. I can't imagine her feeling glad that someone else's life was ruined, the collateral damage spreading out, clawing its way through multiple layers. So, as much as I hate to admit it, maybe Nate is right.

Nate didn't own up to the fact that *he* was the one who ran the red light, though, did he? Why? What game is he playing? But even as I'm thinking it, I know, somehow, that there is no game. I *want* to mistrust him, but I can't quite seem to bring myself to. I saw the way he was recounting the experience, the pain there. Saw it even when I don't think Evie did. I didn't *want* to see it. I don't want to see that kind of emotion from him, don't want to see things from his perspective.

I can feel myself getting pulled back to the day of the accident, with all this thinking about it. Can feel the cool, bright breeze on my face, smell the nutty roast of the coffee shop.

I block it out. I don't want to face that moment because I feel, somehow, that'll be it then. I have no idea if I'm right, of course, other than a *feeling*, but whatever this limbo is, whatever the point of it, it's better than the alternative.

So I direct my thoughts elsewhere instead. I think of the text message Evie got – not the one from her mum, but from mine.

I'm there immediately, in the house where I grew up – the house my parents never left. Mum is sitting in the spare room on the single bed, a blue duvet cover with shooting stars dotted across it. We've always had three bedrooms: my room, which remained mine even after I moved out; my parents' room; and the spare room. I think the spare room was meant for the second child they never had. They never explicitly said that, but I know Mum really wanted another child. She never went into details about *why* it didn't happen, only that 'it wasn't meant to be'. She used to tease me about it, if I ever asked. *Maybe the fates thought we had our hands full with you!* And maybe that's why Evie and I were always so close – sisters by choice, as well as friends.

Mum's face is blotchy, her skin raw-looking, lips chapped. She's usually so religious about her hair appointments – the same hairdresser she's been using for years comes round every six weeks – but now the grey is growing out on top, merging into the brunette. Dad was the blond one, like me, though he's mostly bald now. She's clutching a photo frame. The photo is of me and her together, smiling into the camera, with a beach in the background. Dad took that photo, I remember. We were in Bournemouth. I was seventeen, the last family holiday we all took together – Mum had forced us to go that year, like she knew it was her final chance. I'd mainly moped around, complaining about having nothing to do and no one to go out with, but after that photo was taken, Mum and I had gone off to get our nails done and then gone shopping. We'd got some great buys, and I'd got all excited about some beauties in the charity shops. I was trying to be inventive, mesh things together, practising for my future career – so sure, even then.

'So I reckon that if I chop the arms off *this*,' I'm saying, holding up a green top whose long sleeves are awful: I can see why I wanted to get rid of them, 'and pair it with *this*' – it's a mid-length black skirt – 'then I can make something work.' Mum is sitting on the sofa, cup of tea in hand, and is letting me talk. I purse my lips as I take the rest of the items out of the bags, laying them on the floor of the sitting room of the little house we'd rented for the week. My face is slightly sunburnt. I can feel it, pulling at my skin. I don't remember that. I've always thought I was an expert tanner: brown right away, no red.

'And then when I start—' I look up at the sound of creaking footsteps and see Dad. He's less bald here and he still looks lean, without the paunch that he's developed in the last few years.

'What's this then? Gone a bit wild on the shopping front, have you?' He gives me a wink and I roll my eyes.

'It's all from charity shops, so it's allowed. It's, like, helping the world. Especially if I use this stuff to create *new* things, then it's doubly helping, because I'll give people something new they want to wear that's not actually new.'

Dad laughs. 'Who are you planning to give these "new" clothes to then?' He moves to sit next to my mum, puts an arm around her. I realize I haven't seen that casual, easy gesture between them for a while now.

'No, Dad,' I say, a little impatiently. 'I mean in the future. When I go into fashion.'

Dad sighs. 'Really, Scarlett, still?'

I look up at him from where I'm sitting cross-legged on the floor. 'What do you mean, "still"?'

'I just… I thought you might have moved on from that idea by now. You're finishing school next year, so you need to focus, think of your future.'

'I *am* thinking of my future.' I can still feel the sting that his words leave.

'Yes, but I mean—'

'Leave her be,' Mum says quietly, and Dad drops his arm away from her shoulder.

My temper is coming in, fast. I want to bite back the words. I don't want to snap at my dad like this, not any more. But, of course, I have no control over it. 'Just because *you* didn't follow *your* dream.' I'm not even sure Dad *had* a dream. Did I ever ask him what he'd wanted to do? Or did I take it as a fact that he'd never really had one? That he was happy, being an accountant? I wish I could go back, ask him about it.

Dad sighs again. 'I'm only looking out for you.'

'No,' I retort, 'you're telling me you don't *believe* in me.'

'You're clever, Scarlett,' Dad says earnestly. 'You could do so much more.'

'And who says what is "more"?' Working in a boring office job, that's better, is it? Just because you said so?'

'No, because society says so – they're the jobs that pay the bills.' Dad lifts his hands in a kind of helpless gesture. 'I don't make the rules.'

'Whatever – I don't have to listen to this.' With that, I scoop my new buys off the floor and storm upstairs, making my steps deliberately heavy. I flop down on the single bed, get out my phone. Connor has been messaging me, but I remember thinking it's probably best to make him wait a bit longer. Instead I text Evie.

This holiday is the worst. Wish you were here.

Only two more days! And we've got Green Man in a couple of weeks!

The festival Evie and I went to, I remember – our first. **I can't survive two more days.** So melodramatic.

I have faith. I'm sure you'll have an incredible bonding moment – it'll be like *Cheaper by the Dozen*, only without the other eleven kids.

In the memory, I snort as I put my phone down. But really I should have been grateful, shouldn't I? That my parents *wanted* to take me away, go on holiday. I mean, I'm a teenager, so I suppose it's allowed, but still. Evie never had that, did she? She and her mum never went on holiday together, as far as I can remember.

I can hear my parents arguing downstairs – this cottage is hardly big.

'Why do you rile her like that?' my mum is saying.

'For God's sake, Mel, I'm not riling her, I'm trying to be a responsible parent.'

'She might grow out of it anyway, so what's the point of having an argument about it at this stage?'

I scowl at the idea that Mum, too, doesn't think I can do this. Or didn't, I suppose.

'And if she doesn't?'

'Well, if she doesn't, then we should be supportive.'

'You're too indulgent.'

'I'm not indulgent, Graham, I'm trying to do what's best.'

'You're too lenient,' my dad insists. 'It's like you…'

'Like I what?'

There's a pause, then, 'Nothing.'

'Nothing. Of course.' I can almost imagine my mum screwing up her face at that. Then she sighs. 'We shouldn't argue. We need to be a united front.'

'Get that from one of those parenting books? I thought you'd stopped reading those a while back.'

'Well, some things stay with you.' I hear a clunk. Mum getting up, maybe? Or putting down her tea? 'I'll go up and see Scarlett. She'll be sulking, all alone in her room. It's at times like this I wish…'

'What? You wish what?'

It's Mum's turn to say, 'Nothing' now.

There's quiet for longer than feels entirely comfortable. 'I thought we'd moved past that, Mel. It wasn't meant to be.' My stomach lurches. It's not as if they made it a secret that Mum couldn't get pregnant, but it's still not fun, hearing it out loud. Knowing that Mum didn't get what she longed for. And knowing that, now, the one child she did have – me – has been taken away from her.

I think it's that thought that lurches me back to the present, where Mum is still sitting on the bed. It's evening now – the curtains are open and it's dark outside. I can't work out the way time passes for me, how it works, moving between memory and reality. I don't think I'm even 'here' all the time. Sometimes I think I just drift. The thought scares me, so I shut it down, focus on Mum.

I wish I could speak to her. But what would I say? That I'm okay? I'm not, am I?

There's a knock at the door and Dad steps in. Is it odd that he knocks? I can't quite work it out. 'Are you okay?' he asks. God, he's so grey. Not his hair – though the little hair he has left *is* grey – but the stubble that is growing out, even the pallor of his skin. Grey and lined and old.

Mum looks up and blinks at him, as if coming back from a trance. 'Yes,' she says hoarsely. 'I'm okay.' A lie, if ever I heard one.

'I'm going to bed. Do you need anything before I do?' Mum shakes her head and Dad hesitates. When he does speak, I don't think it's what he really wants to say. 'All right. See you tomorrow.' He shuts the door.

I remember the way he held her, when she broke down at my funeral. Where is that now? Why is he not going to her, comforting her?

Mum stands and opens the chest of drawers. Her clothes. Those are her clothes in those drawers. Something about this routine, it all feels too familiar.

I think back to the last time I was here. It was a few months ago now. I'd been meaning to come for a while, but I'd got busy with work – and Jason, I admit to myself. Anyway the time I *did* come, I'd rung Mum beforehand, to let her know I was setting off. She always came to pick me up from Cambridge train station, even though it was a thirty-minute drive.

'Is Evie coming too?'

'No,' I say after a beat. 'She's not feeling up to it.'

'I hope she's okay.'

'She is. Or she will be. Not the MS,' I add quickly. 'I know that doesn't really get better, but her mind. She'll be feeling more up for things soon,' I try to explain. It's supposed to be phases, after all, and I thought this was a temporary low phase.

'Well, let me know if she changes her mind, okay? I'll

need to move a few things, tidy up the spare room.'

'Why? No one ever sleeps in there.'

'No, no, I know. But I'd need to open the windows, air it out a bit, you know what I mean.'

I'd brushed it off, as I'd brushed off seeing some of Mum's things in the shared bathroom, rather than in her and Dad's en suite. But it hits me now. So maybe being dead really *is* giving me some omniscience. Or maybe it's just making me more observant. Because they've been staying in separate bedrooms for a while now, haven't they? But they've been lying about it. Pretending to stay in the same room when I visited, pretending that everything was okay.

And I'd been too wrapped up in my own drama to even notice.

Chapter Eleven

Evie didn't even really know why she was scrolling through Instagram when she saw the post from Will. She'd been tentatively looking, she supposed, to see if people were still posting about Scarlett. But now she'd seen the post, she couldn't *unsee* it.

A photo of him with his arm around the same girl she'd seen him with before he'd shown up at her door. He was smiling at the camera, that big, toothy white smile. The girl looked more like 'his type' than she did, she thought objectively. She was petite and slim, with perfectly straight, shiny chestnut hair and a matching wide smile that looked ever so slightly fake. As did Will's, actually. They were outside, with rolling green hills in the background, and the caption read: *Quick jaunt to the countryside!*

It was her own damn fault. She shouldn't have let Will kiss her. And she certainly shouldn't have messaged him afterwards, asking if he'd like to meet for coffee.

I'm a bit busy at the moment, but soon, for sure. A brush-off, obviously. Pathetic. *Pathetic, Evie!*

She closed her eyes, tried to imagine what Scarlett would say. *He's the dickwad in this situation, Evie. Not you.*

She started at the sound of a knock at the flat door. Will again? Had she summoned him by thinking about him? She threw the duvet off, got to her feet and padded cautiously through the flat to the front door.

It was indeed a man on the other side. But not Will.

'What are *you* doing here?' She bit the words out, momentarily forgetting that she was still in her pyjamas. At 11 a.m. – 11 a.m. on a *Sunday* morning, but still. They were her ugly flannel checked ones, and she'd been wearing them non-stop for the past week and a half. Not that she cared what Nate thought she looked like. She jutted her chin in the air and resisted the urge to cross her arms over her chest and hide – a small act of defiance. 'How do you know where I live?'

'I'm a journalist, remember? I have my ways.' He said it lightly and she scowled at the effort to be cute. It *wasn't* cute. It was creepy. Invasive. His face grew serious. 'I want to take you somewhere,' he explained, 'and I didn't think you'd agree to go, if I asked you over the phone.'

'So you just showed up, expecting me to be here?'

He shrugged. 'I took a chance.' A chance because she was so clearly that pathetic right now. Evie scowled at herself. There was that word again. 'Please. I want to try and explain why I said what I said to the police. What happened that day.'

She took a step back away from him, but she couldn't stop the words from landing, like little pebbles in her mind. Nate looked at her. She looked at him. Both of them waiting.

'I'm not dressed,' she blurted out. As if *that* was the issue here.

'I'll wait.'

'I need to shower.'

'Okay.' He was so damn calm. It didn't feel right. Wasn't it cutting him up inside? He hadn't known Scarlett, but still – if it was her in his position, she'd be… well, she'd be acting differently.

But she wanted to understand why he was refusing to give a statement against the driver, and whether this was Nate offering to do that. And what was the alternative to going with him? Sitting at home, alone, waiting for tomorrow, when she'd have to face work and the real world again? Henry had already sent her a list of things to do tomorrow, to 'get her up to speed'. A list that included booking an anniversary trip for him and his wife. On a discount. Next weekend.

She gave him a narrow-eyed look. 'You're not an axe murderer are you?'

He grinned, and it was lightning fast. 'No.'

'I suppose if you *were* a murderer, you would say that, though.'

'I never said I wasn't a murderer, just that I wasn't an *axe* murderer. You should be more specific with your questions.'

It didn't make her laugh, but Evie felt the resting scowl on her face soften, a little. 'Where are we going?' She bit her lip. That sounded like she'd already agreed. 'I mean, where do you want to take me?'

He hesitated. 'I can't really tell you – it's more of a *show* kind of situation. But it will make sense at the end, I promise.'

She took a moment, weighing him up. Nate didn't drop the eye contact, but continued to look at her in that level, even way. Most people baulked from her gaze – Scarlett had told her, more than once, that she had a scary stare and she should try to tone it down with new people, but she'd never figured out how to do that. Apparently Nate was immune, though.

'Okay,' she said eventually. 'You can come in and wait while I get ready.'

They drove out of Clapham, heading south-west. Nate had driven to her flat and had parked outside. It was his brother's car, apparently – like the bike. When she'd asked him if he owned anything of his own, he'd shrugged and said, 'Not really. I move around a lot, so my possessions are somewhat limited.'

The radio was on, which negated the need to say anything, and Nate didn't try to push her into any small talk – something Evie couldn't help but appreciate.

They headed into Wimbledon, pulling up opposite the common. It was so green, the trees awake now, blossoms dropping as the leaves got ready for summer. She got out of the car, registering a subtle warmth on her face. May. It would be summer soon, and this place would be crawling with tourists before you knew it, ready for the tennis.

Wimbledon: she and Scarlett had talked about trying to get tickets one year, but they never had. So many things Scarlett would never get to do now.

'This way,' Nate said, jerking his head up the pavement. He led her into a little shop, selling mostly pottery, by the look of things, although there were some candles on display, and a rack of earrings too. The smell of incense lingered in the air, and the shop was bright and open, thanks to the large windows at the front.

'What are we doing here?' she hissed. Maybe she shouldn't have come merrily along with him. She knew nothing about him, after all. Maybe this was some weird front, with some kind of dodgy lair down below. Which was where he was now heading – down the stairs.

She hesitated, then shuffled after him. It was unlikely he was about to murder her, wasn't it? Not in a pottery shop, with other people around.

Most people clocked her stiff gait and tried to help her down stairs, but not Nate. She wondered if it was a lack of consideration on his part, though it felt more like he hadn't noticed. She started down the steps, holding the handrail for support. She'd *expected* him to try to mollycoddle her, she realized. She'd come to expect people to treat her as fragile. It's what Will had done – almost the moment he'd found out about her diagnosis he'd started to treat her as if she were somehow *broken*.

It was darker on the ground floor and it looked a little like a cellar bar, with moody lighting and candles in the corners. There was a bunch of round tables, with children sitting around them, watching a woman at the front of the room. Evie glanced at Nate, waiting for some kind of explanation, but he, too, was looking at the woman, who was adorned with golden bangles and dangling earrings, wearing dark-red lipstick, her curly hair wild, fanning out from her face. She pulled her purple shawl a little closer to her when she saw Nate, but smiled and nodded, then gestured him towards the only free table at the back of the room.

He nudged Evie to it and pulled out a chair for her to sit down. 'What are we—' But the woman starting to speak, and Evie found she couldn't finish her question, getting that feeling of being back at school, where you'd be told off for talking when the teacher was.

'Today we're going to work on your bowls – and it's painting time!'

Evie saw that all the children had clay bowls in front of them, along with paint and paintbrushes. On her and Nate's table there were the paints and the brushes, but no bowls. The woman set the children to work, instructing them on what to do, then came over to Evie and Nate.

'Thanks for coming,' she said warmly to Nate, though Evie couldn't help but notice the way she gripped the edges of the shawl more tightly than seemed necessary.

Nate nodded. 'Tasha, this is Evie. Evie, Tasha.'

'Hello,' Evie said, and it was hard to keep the bafflement out of her voice.

'You missed the clay-making session for the bowls, but you can paint ones that we've already made.' She brought over two bowls. 'You get started – think about what paints you'd like to use. I'll be back, I just have to get the kids going.'

Nate immediately started opening his paints, but Evie just stared at him. 'What on earth are we doing in a pottery class?' What the hell was he playing at?

'Tasha runs the business,' Nate explained, which was not an answer. 'So some of these kids pay to come and do a weekly pottery class, and some of the others can't afford to – they come from disadvantaged backgrounds, and she uses the money from the ones paying to help fund the materials for them, so that they can come and join in too.'

'Okay,' Evie said slowly. 'And what has this got to do with Scarlett?'

But Tasha came over before Nate could answer. 'Paint!' she commanded, lifting her hands and making her gold bangles dance.

Evie jolted and immediately picked up the paintbrush, as if she'd been told off. She reached out to dip the brush in the paint – and the tremor started. It was one of the hardest symptoms to control. She'd tried various medications, but some of them made her too drowsy to function and the others didn't work. Her doctor had said the tremor was notoriously difficult to alleviate with medication – though there were advancements all the time, he'd added quickly.

She swore under her breath and lowered her hand. 'I can't do this,' she muttered.

Nate had his tongue poked out between his teeth as he tried to do lines on the bowl in green. He glanced over at her. 'Why?'

'My hand – it shakes when I try to do stuff like this.' It was hard to keep the bitterness from her voice.

'So why don't you draw a shaky line then? Call it arty.'

'Because…' *Because it will look stupid*, she wanted to say.

'Does it need to be perfect? Mine won't be.' He went back to painting his lines, looking at his bowl rather than at her. But it was all right for him, wasn't it? He didn't have something physical holding him back. 'I used to wish I could be a painter,' he carried on, oblivious to the dark thoughts she was directing at him. 'It was one of my many career ambitions, growing up. That is, until I realized I have absolutely no artistic talent,' he added, with a grin in her direction.

Across the room, a little girl threw down her paintbrush and made a loud grumpy noise, folding her arms. Tasha went over, and Evie heard her patiently explain that they couldn't get mad every time a little detail went wrong. That she should *use* the angst she felt right now, because out of great angst came great art.

Evie felt her lips twitch, just a little, at Tasha's words. Then she sighed. She was being an idiot, for not even trying. Unlike this little girl, she was *not* a child and she couldn't throw a strop about this. It didn't matter, anyway. She told herself that, even as the tremor started the moment she reached for the paintbrush. It didn't matter. It was only a stupid bowl.

A bowl that ended up looking ridiculous. She'd gone with blues and greys and the colours were all over the place, jittery, blending into each other with no control on her part. Though perhaps that was partly because she'd avoided looking at the damn thing as she painted.

She was surprised when Tasha clapped her hands and announced their time was up – when she checked her phone she saw it had been an hour. An hour had gone, and she'd barely noticed it. An hour where she'd not been feeling like she might quite like to be swallowed up by the earth, but an hour where she'd been… well, *distracted*, she supposed, but in the healthy sense of the word, unlike the distraction Will had had in mind.

Tasha beamed as she came over. She laughed a little at Nate's attempt – green and red lines – but kindly, in a way that made Nate grin at her, then made a little noise that genuinely sounded like a purr when she looked at Evie's. 'It's like a stormy sky!' she declared. 'So abstract, I love it.'

Abstract was one word for it, she supposed. Still, she'd done it, hadn't she?

'We'll glaze and fire them,' Tasha said, 'and you can come and pick them up another time.' She gestured them up the stairs, where the kids had already disappeared, and Evie leaned in to whisper to Nate.

'Do we need to pay?'

'Don't worry, I've sorted it.'

Nate turned to face Tasha by the entrance to the shop and Tasha took both his hands in hers. 'You'll come back?'

'I will,' Nate said, squeezing her hands with a gentleness that reminded Evie uncomfortably of when he'd stood with her, outside the church after Scarlett's funeral. 'Whenever I'm in London, I'll make sure to visit.' Some look passed between them, one that Evie couldn't interpret, and Tasha pressed her lips together, as if trying to stop them from trembling. She swallowed, then turned to smile at Evie – a smile that looked a little watery.

'And you, too, Nate's girl. You're welcome any time.'

Evie frowned – mostly at the 'Nate's girl', but also at the fact that she still had no idea who this woman was, or why Nate had brought her to see her.

Nate held the door open for Evie and she stepped outside, slipping on her denim jacket. She breathed in the fresh air, chasing away the lingering smell of paint. She glanced up at Nate, found his coffee eyes looking directly at her.

'Umm, that was all very nice and everything,' she said, 'but I still don't understand. How is this supposed to explain anything?' She shoved her hands in her pockets as they started walking back to his car. Her anger at him had dissipated over the hour of painting, and she wasn't quite sure how to act around him as a result.

He said nothing, and she glanced up to see him staring out at the common. 'Because, Evie.' Then he looked back at her. 'Because that woman – Tasha – she's the person who hit Scarlett.'

Chapter Twelve

Fuck! I was not expecting that. I didn't know what Nate was planning. I imagined he was taking Evie on some kind of weird day-trip to make her forgive him. And she was thawing, a little. I know she doesn't *want* to thaw, but she was, with the bloody pottery and the kids and the whole fucking cliché of it all.

Like Patrick Swayze in Ghost, I would say to Evie, in a world where I'm still alive, sitting at home, while she's out on this… well, it's *not* a date, but it could theoretically be one, if everything was different, couldn't it?

Exactly like Patrick Swayze in Ghost! she'd say back.

The irony is not lost on me – that film is the perfect reference, not because of the pottery, but because I am here, watching them.

I see Evie's green eyes spark with hurt, with anger. I feel it too. That woman was the one who hit me? With the bangles and the fucking shawl? The feel of the car slamming into the top of my legs comes back to me, followed by the taste of blood. Memories I didn't realize I had, because it was all over so quickly, at the time.

'What?' Evie is saying. 'How do you…?'

'I saw her,' Nate explains, his voice low, quiet. 'When she got out of the car that day, to see what had happened.' His body quakes with the next breath he takes.

The fucking cheek of him! As if *he* is traumatized by it. He is not the one who is dead, is he? And, Jesus, that woman. Tasha.

'I tracked her down later. I wanted to…' He doesn't finish that sentence. I wonder if he even knows where it was going, what he wanted to say. I wish I *did* know.

'I can't believe you.' Evie's voice is a whisper, but it's cutting. 'I can't believe you brought me here to… what? What are you trying to prove?' Her voice grows louder. Not quite shouting – she's good at avoiding that – but loud enough that a few people turn their heads to look. I'm not sure Evie notices. 'Are you trying to *manipulate* me—' She cuts herself off, turns from him, and I know: she is trying to get out of there, before whatever she has banked inside her bubbles over. It makes me *ache* – actually ache – to see her trying to keep it all in, to feel how much this must be hurting her.

Nate reaches out a hand to grab her, but she shakes it off. She turns to him, though, pushing her hair out of her face. 'And, what: you're making it some kind of moral judgement? Because she's a "good person" – whatever that means – and therefore doesn't need to punished? She *killed* my best friend. Don't you get that?'

It rolls through me, like nausea that you can't control. She killed me. That woman *killed* me. And for a moment that burns, hot and dark at the same time.

Then it ebbs, slowly. Because I know – like I know Nate does – that there is nothing Tasha could have done. I didn't look. I didn't fucking *look* before I stepped into the road to get his bike. *His* bike, because he'd been cycling like an idiot. But regardless of whether Nate holds some blame for that, I don't think Tasha does. I shouldn't have run into the road like that. And I know, deep down, that Tasha should not be punished for that. Evie will know that too, in time.

But right now she's crying, and though I don't want to, I see the way Nate's expression twists at that, the anguish there. 'Look,' he says desperately, 'I'm not trying to…'

But he can't finish – again. He's the type of person to speak without really thinking, it seems, and then he gets stuck. He certainly *acted* without thinking, didn't he? Exactly the opposite of Evie. Maybe he doesn't even know why he brought her here, what point he was trying to prove. Fuck, did he even think it all the way through?

'It doesn't matter whether the person was good or awful,' he says. 'They are a person, with their own life, and going to prison… it could fuck you up.' The way he says that last part: there is something there, I'm sure of it. Something that I don't think Evie has noticed. Has he been to prison? He doesn't look like he has, but then how the hell does someone look like they've been to prison? I imagine bald heads, big muscles, tattoos, and I know I'm being ridiculous.

'I know that,' Evie snaps. She closes her eyes briefly, and I realize she's regretting the barbed tone. I know that she's worried where this anger will lead her. She hasn't always been like this, so desperate to bury her feelings. But then I suppose she hasn't always had so much to be angry about. 'But some people deserve it,' she whispers.

'Some do, yeah,' he agrees. 'But not in this case.' He hesitates, then says softly, 'It was an accident. A horrible accident.'

Tears spring to Evie's eyes again and I feel an answering crack within me. An *accident*.

Not inevitable. Just something that happened because I was in the wrong place at the wrong time. Because I made a series of decisions that day – and so did Nate.

'I'm sorry. I'm so sorry, Evie.'

'Stop saying that,' she sobs. She shakes her head, and the action looks frantic. 'I don't know what to do. I wanted to find the person who killed her, to…' She gulps in air, and I realize she doesn't actually know what she was going to do when she found this person, and right then I feel a flare of hate for Nate, for forcing it on her. He should have let her come to this in her own damn time. 'And now what? I can't go back in there, can't face that woman. I don't know…'

Her sobbing breaths are coming quicker now. Nate shoves his hands into his pockets, and I see the tension in his body, the way he is holding himself so tight. He wants to touch her. I've seen it enough times, that body language – have become an expert on it, in fact. Not only with Jason, but men in general. I know when they want to touch me, and right then I know Nate wants to touch Evie. He doesn't, though. Like he knows it would only make things worse.

'That's okay,' he says instead. 'You don't have to. If you never want to see her again, then that's fine. But now you know.'

She rubs her hands over her face. 'Weren't you afraid I'd go all *Psycho* on her?' There is a touch of bitterness in her voice, but I can tell what she's doing here. She is trying to diffuse something between them – the way she did with me, the morning of my death. She also doesn't mean it like 'psycho', as in going crazy. She means it as in *Psycho*, the film, with the black-and-white woman holding the dagger in the shower. Nate doesn't get that, though.

'I didn't really think of that, to be honest.' He rubs the back of his neck, as if realizing for the first time that he should have thought about it. '*Are* you going to? Do you want to go back in there, speak to her?'

'Yes,' Evie says harshly. But she stays still, makes no move to walk back over there. She *wants* to want to confront Tasha, I know. Feels like she should, maybe. But I'm pretty sure she won't. 'She hit Scarlett,' she says numbly. 'Tasha hit her. She killed her.'

Nate steps towards her, closing a little of the space between them so that she has to tilt her chin, ever so slightly, to meet his gaze. He's taller than her – only slightly, but still. 'Look, Evie. It wasn't Tasha's fault. If anything...'

Shit, he's going to do it. He's actually going to man up and tell her. I don't know why, but the thought makes me panic slightly, and I feel myself trying to occupy the space between them, trying to stop him. Which is stupid. He *should* tell her. And he should be feeling awful about it. Maybe it's because I know she's had enough. But, of course, I have no control – all I can do is watch.

'I wasn't concentrating,' Nate admits. 'I was on my phone, riding one-handed, and I ran through a light at the last minute and…' He looks down at the pavement rather than at her. 'I wasn't looking, so when a car nearly hit me, that's why I fell. And that's why Scarlett stopped, to help me.'

The moment I saw him, riding that red bike, flashes through my mind. Evie is staring at Nate. He looks up, and for a second their gazes meet. Then, without a word, she spins away from him.

He lurches after her, and it strikes me now that this is a pattern they're falling into – her leaving, him chasing her. 'Evie, wait.'

'No,' she says sharply, still with her back to him. 'I can't deal with this right now. I can't deal with *you*. I'm leaving.'

Nate has a longer stride than her, and she walks slowly as it is, so it's barely a second before he catches up with her, moving around Evie and stopping in front, so that she's forced to stop too. She tries to dodge past him, and he moves to block her. It would be almost comical, if not for the situation.

'Wait,' he says again. 'Let me at least drive you home.' His voice has a pleading edge to it.

'No,' Evie says shortly. But she's stopped trying to move around him, and her shoulders are sagging, deflated. 'I think you should leave.'

'But I—'

'*You* are the reason she is dead.' Her body starts to grow then, her spine straightening, chin lifting. Maybe Nate won't notice, but I know her well enough to see the build, the way her body must be heating with anger. 'That's what you're telling me, isn't it? I already…' She shakes her head, but the words she doesn't say are obvious. *I already blamed you.* 'You were careless, and it didn't cost you *your* life, it cost *hers*.'

'I know. Jesus, I know, and I'm just trying to make up for—' He breaks off, wincing slightly.

'*Make up* for it?' She stares at him incredulously. 'You can't *make up* for something like that – it's not a fucking balancing act!' There it is. Finally. There's the temper, unleashed. I see it, bubbling over, her body practically vibrating with it. 'I have to try to *deal* with this all somehow. I have to pack up her things, I have to find a new place to live.' She swipes angrily at a tear that has escaped. 'I can't do this, don't you understand? I have to go back to work tomorrow and face reality, and my boss wants me to book a last-minute trip for his *stupid, insignificant* anniversary, somewhere brilliant at no cost, and if I don't pull it off, then that may very well be the last straw for him and I will be *fired*, and I can't lose my job because my damn MS means I can't get another one all that easily and—'

'I can help with that,' Nate interrupts.

She hitches in a breath. 'What?'

He clears his throat. 'I mean, I have travel contacts. I could help with the trip.'

'I don't *want* your help,' she snaps back. 'I don't want to be the person you help, so that you can feel *better* about what happened.' Nate says nothing, and I wonder if it's true – if he's trying to help her because he genuinely wants to, or just to alleviate his guilt. 'What were you expecting?' Evie carries on, her voice bitter. 'That you'd bring me here and explain, and I'd smile and say, "Thank you, now I can move on"? Or that you'd tell me what happened and I'd pat *you* on the back, tell you it wasn't your fault? Because it was!' Her voice is too tight, like she's struggling to get the words out. 'It *was* your fault, and Tasha's, and…' Her tears are coming faster, tracing twin paths down her pale face.

Almost like he can't help himself this time, Nate steps forward, lays a hand on her arm.

'Don't touch me!' she screams, and he jerks back. 'Scarlett is gone. She's *gone*, and none of this will *make it better*, none of this will bring her back. It's all very well for you – you didn't know her. You can move on and forget about her and your life won't change, but mine… She was my best friend, the one person I would always choose to spend time with, and now I don't have anyone else and I…' She can't speak through her tears any more, and she sinks down onto the pavement, giving in to the sobs and wrapping her arms around her knees. There, in public, crying on the side of the road, with a line of shops behind her.

And God, it's torture. I want to tell her that I'm still here. Tell her that I'm sorry, for leaving her that morning. To tell her that she'll be okay.

Nate is standing there, staring at her, hovering in indecision. *Do something*, I urge him. Because yes, he is not my first choice and he is careless and inconsiderate and *reckless*, but right now he is the only choice there is. I know he can't hear me. Honestly, logically, I know it. But there is a part of me that feels victorious as he moves to sit beside her on the pavement.

110

He doesn't say anything. He doesn't touch her. He just sits next to her, in silence.

'Go away,' Evie says through her tears, tightening her grip on her knees. He says nothing, mirroring her posture instead, so that he sits shoulder-to-shoulder with her on the kerb, wrapping his arms around his knees and looking straight ahead. A few people give them funny looks as they pass, but if Nate notices, he ignores them.

'Please, just leave,' she whispers. Her sobs are settling a bit, her body stiller.

He shakes his head. 'I'm not going to leave you.' A statement of fact, one that allows no room for argument. And for the first time I think that maybe there is something more to him. That maybe there is a part of him that's not completely selfish.

She turns to him, tears shining in her eyes. 'Why?'

'Because…' He blows out a breath. 'Because I know what it's like to feel sad and alone.'

I think of my funeral.

Been to many, have you?

One.

'And I might not be able to help with the sad part,' he continues, 'but, at least for now, I can do something about the alone.'

If I could hold my breath, I would. Evie doesn't say anything to that, though. She rests her gaze on Nate for a long moment, then looks out at the common and all that green.

And they both sit there in silence, until Evie's tears stop. Silent and alone. But alone together.

Chapter Thirteen

For the third time in a row that week Evie left the house earlier than she needed to, giving herself plenty of time to get to Waterloo, where her office was. Scarlett had said she was 'giving up' when she'd first taken the job – a full-time permanent position as opposed to all the temping she'd been doing. She'd seen it as Evie deciding that she wasn't even going to *try* to make playing music a reality – was giving up on her dream for good. And maybe she'd been right, Evie thought. Maybe she'd given up even before her diagnosis, with the constant auditions and many rejections wearing her down.

And now she was stuck doing something she hated. Because she had discovered over the past few years that she had zero interest in advertising. Why were they always trying to sell people more stuff? Didn't everyone already have enough stuff? Not that she ever voiced that opinion at work, where meetings revolved around how to 'sex up' kitchenware or how to convince people that a certain brand of watch would buy you love and respect.

She slowed her pace as she reached the ground floor of the block of flats. Astrid was there, looking out of the frosted glass that made up the top half of the front door. She was in a school uniform – black trousers, loose-fitting blazer, tie. Her hair was tied into a bun on the top of her head, the same way Evie had seen her wearing it when she'd met her a few days ago.

Evie came to a stop in the small entrance hall. 'Hello, Astrid.'

Astrid looked over to her, gnawing at her lip. She was clutching a school bag in one hand – a one-strap, plain black bag. 'I have to go to school,' she said, a little redundantly.

Evie nodded slowly. 'I have to go to work.'

'At least you get paid.'

'True,' Evie agreed – she'd had the same perspective as a kid too, the idea that at least the teachers got *paid* to be there. Although right now she'd give anything to go back to school, return to when Scarlett was still alive and she hadn't had an illness, and everything still seemed bright and shiny and *possible*.

'It's my second day. Mum let me have Monday off, but she won't let me stay at home any more. Yesterday was *horrible*, and it's the last term and everyone already knows each other, and I don't understand half of what the teachers are banging on about and they're already talking about GCSEs, which don't even start until next year – as if I want to be panicking about that already.' She said it all in one breath, then gulped in air when she was done.

Evie tried to work it out: if GCSEs started next year, then... 'How old are you?'

'Thirteen.'

Astrid looked young for thirteen – though maybe that

was because she wore clothes like she was hiding under them: loose and baggy.

'Maybe you should join a club. At school. You know,' Evie said when Astrid frowned at her, 'to make friends.' Astrid gave her a Look, and Evie realized she sounded like *that* adult. 'Or not,' she said on a sigh. 'Either way, we should probably both go. Slave to the institution and all that.'

'What?'

'Nothing.' Evie stepped towards the door, but Astrid didn't move – and she was still in the way.

'There's an orchestra,' Astrid said. 'And a music club. There's this, like, social officer or something, who gave me the rundown of all the clubs yesterday. But I don't want to do it.' She glanced up at Evie. 'Did you do it? Play at school?'

Evie hesitated, then nodded. 'Yeah.'

'Did you enjoy it?'

'Yeah.' She blew out a breath, remembering the feel of the violin pressed against her body, the way the bow slid between her fingers, how she'd been able to close her eyes and just *be* every time she played. 'Yeah, I enjoyed it. Not the performing part, but I liked being a part of something.' She didn't know why she said that. It sounded stupid.

'Well, I don't want to,' Astrid was saying. 'I want to be back at my old school.'

'How come you had to move?'

She made a face. 'We used to live in North London. Mum tried to find a place there but couldn't afford anything, and my old school is too far away, apparently –

Mum doesn't want me travelling all that way, and now I'm in a different district anyway, or whatever. Dad still lives there,' she mumbled. 'I think that's the real reason Mum didn't find a place there. He went off with someone else, but he's still there and they are living in *my* house now. He left *us*, but he gets the house. How is that fair?'

'It's not,' Evie said simply.

Astrid blinked up at her, looking like she'd expected Evie to say something else. 'Yeah. It's not. Anyway, which way are you going?'

Evie raised her eyebrows at the abrupt change of subject. 'Towards Clapham Junction.'

'Cool. Me too. We can walk together.'

Astrid opened the door, but Evie hesitated, feeling the pressure of being the responsible adult in this situation. 'You *are* going to go to school, aren't you?' She glanced around. 'Where's your mum?'

'She had to leave early for work – I said I'd get there myself. Anyway, I do *not* want to be seen walking in with my mum.'

'Fair enough.' Evie stepped out of the door. It was raining. Only spitting, but still. She fumbled in her handbag for her umbrella. So much for the bright, sunny May of the weekend. 'You're not going to bunk or anything, are you?' Evie asked, glancing at Astrid, still not sure if she should be doing something more 'adult-like'.

'Bunk? Oh, you mean skive? Nah. I mean, I thought about it, but I don't think Mum could take it if I did.'

Evie nodded. 'Well, all right then. Let's walk.'

Evie slid into her desk at work, smiled at Suzy, the other assistant, when she came in not long after.

'Morning, chickadee,' Suzy said as she sat down.

She had a motherly kind of look, Suzy, with an approachable, round face, an easy smile and hair that she was already letting grow out grey, even though she was just shy of forty, because 'It would cost a fortune to keep up with it, otherwise'. She had two kids, Evie knew. Maybe that was where the motherly vibe came from – maybe everyone *became* motherly after having kids. Though that hadn't worked on her mum, so maybe not.

'Cola bottle?' Suzy asked, offering Evie the packet of sweets.

Evie shook her head. She watched as Suzy helped herself to one, despite the fact it was not quite 9 a.m. yet. She imagined the cola bottles screaming to one another, to Suzy, *Don't eat me-e-e-e-e.* Shame. Poor cola bottles.

Everyone was starting to come in now – it might be early, but it was the type of office where you got brownie points for being visible, and everyone knew it. And, of course, Henry was the first to come marching over.

'You look well, Evie,' he said by way of 'good morning'. It wasn't a compliment, she'd learned that long ago. It was something he'd started saying semi-regularly since she'd been diagnosed, as if to point out that she didn't *look* sick and therefore she should be getting on with things like 'the rest of them'. 'How are the weekend plans coming along? My wife has high expectations – I don't want to let her down.'

Well, why don't you sort it yourself then, you lazy prick? It was Scarlett's voice in her mind, though, and out loud all Evie said was, 'I'm working on it.'

As Henry walked away, she groaned. 'What am I going to do, Suzy? There is no way I'm going to find something now.' She'd already spent two days ringing around hotels, with no luck whatsoever – no one was willing to give her a discount, which was obvious, because no one knew who Henry was. He might think he was a bigshot in London, but really he was no one. 'There's no way, and then what will happen? What's he going to say?' She felt anxiety bubble up inside her, because for all her thoughts of life being easier if she didn't have this job, she was well aware of how much she needed it.

Suzy flapped a hand. 'Just don't do it. He can't fire you for it – it would be a nightmare with HR.' Helpful. Really bloody helpful.

'No, but he can fire me *because* of it and say it was for something else, officially.'

Suzy had no answer to that, and Evie opened up her in-box, started clearing her emails to distract herself. She frowned when she got to the third one down:

Dear Miss Jenkins,

We are delighted to confirm your stay with us at The Balmoral Hotel, Edinburgh. The Junior Suite has been reserved for this weekend, checking in Friday 13 May, checking out Monday 16

May. Two spa treatments will be included in the package, as well as breakfast and dinner in our award-winning restaurant. If you have any questions, please do not hesitate to contact us.

Kind regards,

The Reservations Team

She read the email through again. She hadn't called this hotel. It was expensive, well out of Henry's price range, and she felt a rising swell of panic as she tried to remember if maybe she *had* tried to book this in the last two days, what with the number of places she'd been contacting. Her neurologist had warned her that MS could cause cognitive problems too, as well as the physical ones, and whilst she'd had no sign of that yet, maybe this was the first – a little memory slip. She felt her heart thud painfully.

She rang the hotel, asked to speak to the Reservations Team.

'Hello, you're through to Katie, how can I help?'

'Yes, hello, this is Evie Jenkins. I've just received an email from you – I think there may be some kind of mistake. It's a confirmation email for a booking this weekend, but I never actually placed a booking, so I wanted to find out if...' *If what, Evie?* If she was losing her mind, as well as her body?

'Okay, if you'll bear with me, please.' Evie could imagine exactly the type of person the voice belonged to – someone with a bright, sunny smile.

She was put on hold until a different person, a man this time, picked up the phone.

'Hello, this is the manager speaking.'

Evie started to launch into the same explanation, but she only got as far as her name before the man interrupted her. 'Ah yes. Nate's girl.'

Nate's girl. The echo of Tasha's words made Evie wince. He'd sat with her. Sat with her as she'd cried, until she'd felt so exhausted she could barely stand, and then she'd let him help her up and back to his car. They'd been quiet the whole way back to her flat, but something had shifted and she hadn't been sure what to make of it.

'Nate?' she echoed now.

'Yes. He's agreed to write a lovely piece for us, in exchange for a bit of a discount.' The manager named the price, and Evie felt her heart thud. 'A bit of' was putting it nicely. 'It's for your boss, is that right?'

'Yes,' Evie said, still feeling like she was playing catch-up. She remembered her rant. *I can help with that.* But Nate hadn't brought it up again, and she'd thought nothing of it.

'Yes. Well, Nate's been to stay with us before for a travel piece – and he reckons he can get us in the "Top ten places to stay in Scotland", so don't you worry about a thing. Any friend of Nate's is a friend of ours. What's your boss's name? I'll get his name rather than yours put on the system, shall I?'

She gave the manager Henry's details, and then had the presence of mind to ask him to email again to confirm everything, just to be sure this wasn't some kind of trick. When they hung up, Evie stared at the phone. It had been *Nate's* doing. Well, at least that meant she wasn't losing her memory.

Suzy glanced over at her. 'What's happened, chick? All okay?'

'I don't…' She shook her head. 'I've found a place, for Henry's trip this weekend.'

'That's good then. Why do you look so upset about it?'

'Because…' She launched into an explanation about Nate – who he was, the fact that he'd gone behind her back to sort this for her.

Suzy nodded along. 'I'll admit it sounds a little complicated, but I wouldn't say he's gone behind your back, chickadee.'

'But he didn't even *tell* me about it.'

'Well, maybe he didn't want to take the credit.'

'Suzy, did you not listen to me? Did you not hear what he did?'

'Yes, I did.' She helped herself to another cola bottle. 'But maybe try to put yourself in his shoes, hmm? Makes sense that he'd want to make things better for you.'

Evie recoiled slightly. *Make up* for it, he'd said. She still hated the words. And she didn't *want* to be grateful to Nate. How had he even found out where she'd worked, got her email address? Then again, that wasn't such a mystery – he was a journalist, as he'd pointed out, and all her details were on the company website. She was embarrassingly easy to cyber-stalk, it seemed.

She sent the email through to Henry – she was hardly going to refuse, given her situation – and got a 'Good 'work' back. She let out a long breath, just as her mobile rang.

It was the same unknown number that had tried to ring her a few times now – she was starting to recognize the digits. After a quick glance around the office to see if Henry was anywhere nearby, she answered it.

'Hello?'

'Is that Evie?'

'Yes.' Evie frowned – she didn't recognize the voice. 'Who is this?' She saw Suzy give her a look out of the corner of her eye.

'Jason. We've never met, but I'm—'

'I know who you are,' Evie said coldly. An image came to her then, of Scarlett crying on the sofa. *I love him, Eves.*

'Right. Right. Well, as you know,' he said with an air of formality, 'I worked with Scarlett a few times and we're... There's a team of us trying to pull together some last pieces of hers. We wanted to see if the investors were still interested in taking the label forward. It would be in her name,' he added quickly. 'A chance for her dream to come true, even if...' His voice cracked then, the formal tone breaking. He blew out an audible breath. 'We were wondering: are there any designs of hers at her flat? Any drawings, pieces she might not have shown anyone yet? We have a few, but we want to see what else we can pull together. And we'd do a shoot, so that we have something to show them and... I'm sorry. I'm getting ahead of myself.' His formal, professional tone returned. 'I just... I didn't know who else to ask. I know you lived together. I know you two were close. So I thought if anyone would know, it would be you.'

Evie stayed quiet for a moment, listening to the sound of her heart as she processed what he'd said. Scarlett's label – a chance for her designs, her own ideas, to be produced. It was something she would have wanted, she was sure of it.

'I don't know,' she said eventually. 'I'm sorry.' And she meant it. 'I suppose it's a possibility. When is all this happening?'

'Nothing is confirmed yet. It's just… an idea, at this stage.'

'I'll have a look,' Evie said, before she could think better of it, before she could imagine the way that digging through Scarlett's things was bound to make her crumble. 'I'll call you on this number if I find anything.'

'All right. Thanks, Evie.'

Evie hesitated, wondering if she should say anything else to him, this man who had been the cause of so much heartache for her best friend. But all she ended up actually saying was, 'Sure.' Some things, she decided, you could not say over the phone.

So many things would have to go unsaid, now that Scarlett was gone. All the conversations, the arguments, the laughter that would have happened if she'd not stepped off the pavement that day would now be lost, a different reality stepping in to sweep them away.

Chapter Fourteen

Jason called Evie. He actually *called* her. And what he wants to do… well, it proves how much he cared about me, doesn't it? I feel a sudden rush of warmth. He wants to do something to keep my memory alive. And *I* want it. I really, really want it. It was always a driving factor for me – not the only one, but definitely a big part of it. The idea that people would know my name, would be saying that they had gone out and bought an exclusive Scarlett Henderson.

I want details. Why didn't Evie ask for more details? She's still sitting there, staring at her phone, in that depressing prison of an office. I've never seen her office before, and she's never told me quite how bleak it is – all uniform grey and white, blinds half drawn over the windows so that the artificial light can have its time to shine. You'd think at an advertising agency there would be more vibrancy and colour. I want her to get up, go back home, start looking. I wish she'd storm out of there right now – she should anyway, because she's completely wasting herself at that job, I've told her that enough times.

There's definitely one piece at the flat that they could use, I'm sure of it. Evie would find it without too much effort. Though the warmth fades as I think of it. I didn't design that one to be shared with the world – that was for one person, and one alone. I shouldn't be thinking of it like that. But there might be others, and even if not, Jason might have enough of what he needs from my office, as presumably he's called there too.

Jason. I haven't checked in on him, for obvious reasons. Haven't wanted to see what he's doing now, how he's spending his time. I never really wanted to know the details of his home life when I was alive, so why should it be any different now that I'm dead? But I find my mind drifting back now, thinking of him. Thinking of the moment I met him.

I was at a party, a work event. It was right after Evie had been diagnosed – I hadn't wanted to leave her home alone, but Evie had insisted. *You have to network for your job, right? You're never going to be some superstar designer if you don't, and I refuse to be the reason you miss something important. So go. Work those nets.*

I'm with Ben, a guy from work, both of us standing at the edge of the crowd, sipping champagne. It's a cool, underground venue, with stone walls and low lighting, candles flickering around the edges. It's ridiculous, really, for a label launch – you need to be able to *see* the clothes, and the lighting is shifting the focus, making things look more sultry and moody than they really are. Though maybe that's the point. This label never actually took off; after the launch it sort of faded. So maybe they knew it wasn't quite up to scratch in the cold, hard light of day.

'I always feel like an imposter at these things,' Ben mutters, glancing around the room, then adjusting his waistcoat. He's slim and pole-like, but despite his less-than-ideal body shape, and despite his ginger hair, which makes certain colours off-limits, he always looks right on trend. It had been our boss who suggested both of us come tonight to represent the company. She didn't have the time, she'd said, and I knew that it was because she didn't deem the launch important enough, but I didn't care. A launch was a launch – and you never knew who you might meet.

'Just act like you belong,' I murmur, taking a sip of my ever so slightly warm champagne. I can taste it, exactly as it was then – and it hits me that I will never drink champagne again, never feel the fizzing in my mouth, the slide of it down my throat, the brilliant light-headedness that comes after two glasses. I want to lift my arm, take another sip, but I have to wait until the me of the past decides to do so.

Ben sighs. 'Easy for you to say, you always look like you belong.'

'That's because I've learned to be a good actor.' I wink, and Ben laughs. He left the company about six months after this and although we both promised to stay in touch, we haven't spoken to each other since – life running away with us. Does he even know I'm dead? Probably, what with social media, but I can't be sure. How long will it take for the news to spread, until everyone I've ever had a connection with knows?

Ben steps in a little closer to me, nods over to the other side of the room. 'There's a guy over there watching you,' he says, his voice low.

I sip my champagne again – *yes!* – and wait a beat before I turn. I see him immediately. Tall, muscled shoulders shown off by a sleek black jacket, chiselled jaw and dark, brooding eyes. God, he's attractive. I feel the rush of it wash through me, even now. And he's so *cool*. He always was.

I shoot Ben a wicked grin. 'Well, I better go and see what he wants then, hadn't I? Don't have too much fun without me.' I give him another wink. Who am I: all this winking? Did I really used to wink so much?

I'd recognized him immediately, of course, though I'd not yet worked with him at that stage. I didn't go to the shoots often back then, and even since, I only went to a handful. It's one of those aspects of the jobs that I thought I'd be doing all the time – dashing off to photoshoots and charming models (until I got big enough that *they* had to charm *me*), but the reality's a little different.

He's not looking at me directly as I walk over to him, but I can sense his attention lingering. I know I look great as I walk – I've practised it enough times. Shoulders back, head high, graceful on my heels. Quick enough that I look busy, important, but not so quick that I look awkward and rushed. It's a walk that has become so natural to me that I barely notice I'm doing it. This kind of performance is a part of me now. Always act like there is someone watching, because there *might* be someone watching.

'Hello,' I say as I reach him, and his attention snaps to me, so fast that I know I was right – he'd tracked my movements across the room. His eyes. God, his eyes! Dark

126

on the outside and lightening towards the middle, giving them a kind of fiery glow. I'd felt the spark of attraction instantly, and even now his very presence engulfs me.

I take a sip of champagne, studying him over the rim of the glass. 'You're Jason Ballard,' I state. 'The photographer.'

He raises one eyebrow. 'Am I now?' He's semi-famous, at least within the industry.

'I'm Scarlett,' I say, with a small curve of my lips.

'Hello, Scarlett. And you are, what: a model?' He flashes me a grin, showing me it's just a line, that he knows I'm not. I'm too bloody short, for one thing. But I laugh anyway, playing the game.

'I'm a designer.'

'Are you now?' he says in that same tone of voice. 'How come I've never heard of you?'

'Junior designer,' I explain, wrinkling my nose a little before I realize that might be unattractive. 'But not for long.'

'Somehow I believe that.' Our gazes lock, and I feel the tingle right through my core. I'd seen photos of him, of course, and whenever anyone said his name at work someone would sigh – a little joke that got replayed over and over. But none of that had quite prepared me for meeting him in person.

'Can I get you another glass of champagne?' he asks, glancing at my near-empty flute.

I smile. 'I'd love that, but they said they're all out – it was arrival champagne only, apparently, and it's all about the cheap white wine now.' I regret the words once they're out – he might have a relationship with the designers, after all – but Jason grins.

'Nothing like the old glory days,' he says, with a mock shake of his head.

'So I've been told.' My boss was always on about how much better the launches used to be.

'Still,' Jason says, 'I'm sure they'd let us buy a couple of glasses. Or,' he continues, his voice lowering a fraction, 'I know a good champagne bar down the road. We could go, have a glass of something nicer.'

I feel his body shift. Not touching me, not yet, but close enough that an awareness of his physical presence shoots through me. My body reacts to it, my nerves fizzing. I've literally never had that reaction with anyone but him – before or after. I glance around the room and bite my lip, see him track the movement with his gaze.

'Trust me,' he says, 'there's no one here worth speaking to.' He knew, then, what I was thinking – the fact that I was supposed to be a 'presence' here. 'You and I are the most interesting people here by far,' he adds, and my skin tingles at the way he says 'you and I'. Besides, people are already filtering out, aren't they? There's no sign of Ben – either he's left or he's found someone to speak to.

And so I put my empty flute down, allow him to get my coat and follow him up out of the party and to the champagne bar, where he'll buy me another two glasses and we'll chat and laugh about nothing.

We didn't sleep together that night. We didn't even kiss. But it was like being swept up in a wave from that moment on – there was an inevitability to it that I never wanted to fight. And by the time I did, it was too late.

I think of the message, still sitting on my phone, wherever it is now.

Meet me before you go into work today. I want to see you.

He'd have seen me at the party, later that evening, but that wasn't the kind of 'seeing' Jason was on about.

I still don't know what I would have said, what I would have done. I still don't know if I would have caved, one last time.

Chapter Fifteen

The moment Evie got out of the car and smelled the salt of the sea, felt the warm breeze on her face, she regretted her decision to come. Actually she'd regretted it when she'd first got in the car, but it really hit her now. Nate had not said much over text, other than that he needed to go to a beach in Somerset to write up a piece and, since he could do with a second opinion on the subject at hand, would she like to come? And because she'd felt like she owed him, after he'd helped her out with Henry's trip, even though he'd never demanded any gratitude, she'd ended up saying yes. She suspected he might be making it up – the fact that he needed a second opinion – but it had worked, hadn't it?

She hadn't spoken to Tasha in the end, hadn't known what to say. She'd thought about it in hindsight, remembered the sad look that had passed between Tasha and Nate, the way they were now bonded over something so awful. Maybe she'd go back there or maybe she wouldn't – because what would it change, really? But Nate had been right about one thing: she didn't want to see Tasha locked up. And she didn't think Scarlett would have wanted that, either. Maybe initially, in anger, but after that… well, it did no one any good, did it?

Nate glanced down at her as he came round to her side of the car. His words from the other day came to her unbidden. *Because I know what it's like to feel sad and alone. And I might not be able to help with the sad part, but, at least for now, I can do something about the alone.* And whether she admitted it to herself or not, that was another reason she'd agreed to come with him today.

'Shall we?' Nate asked and gestured across the car park. She nodded, only risking a quick glance at him, then scanning the surroundings as they started down the steps that led to the rocky beach. There was no sand in sight – the waves foamed against rocks and pebbles, which gave way to a green cliff edge above. It was more of a brisk and bracing walk-type beach rather than one the tourists flocked to for sunbathing, although there were a few people out with towels having a go at it, in true English fashion, and a couple of kids splashing in the waves. It was June, admittedly – though only just – and the sun was warm today against a brilliant blue sky, but it was not warm enough for *that*, as far as Evie was concerned.

She felt the familiar stiffness in her muscles as they reached the bottom of the steps. It was morning, though, and she was usually better in the mornings. She held on to that – the hope that she'd get through this without too much drama.

'You never told me why we're here,' she said to Nate as he turned right. 'How come you need a second opinion: it's a beach, how opinionated can you be?'

He grinned – that smile that seemed to come so naturally to him. What must it be like to have everything roll off you, to be able to smile that easily? 'You'd be surprised. You can have a *lot* of opinions about a lot of places, even if objectively they all look the same. I did a "Top ten beaches in Europe" piece once.'

'Was it as glamorous as it sounds? Sitting on a beach, drinking pina coladas?'

'Absolutely. Well, some of it was. But they're not actually going to pay for you to go around all the beaches, so some of it's just sitting in the Airbnb on Google. I did write it in Crete, though.'

'I went to Crete once,' Evie said, remembering.

'Really?'

'Yeah. With Scarlett.' They both fell quiet at that and Evie frowned at herself. She was trying not to do that. Mentioning her name around Nate, it felt like a… betrayal, somehow. A betrayal of Scarlett: that she was here with the person who was, unintentionally, the cause of her death.

An accident. The word kept rolling around her mind, her brain trying to come to terms with it.

'So,' she said, trying to make her voice a little brighter, 'is this a "Top ten beaches of England" thing? Top-ten places to come to, if you want to feel all moody as you watch the waves crash, that type of thing?'

'It *is* a bit on the moody side, isn't it?'

'If Heathcliff were to show up here, I wouldn't be surprised.' Evie held up her hands. 'That's all I'm saying.'

Nate gave her another grin as they approached some

kind of shop – or shack, really. It was painted bright red and there were picnic benches on a deck outside, with big umbrellas, like people could sit and have coffee there.

'It's this new adventure-climbing thing on the beach,' Nate said, 'and they want a first-hand write-up. For a little magazine I've done some work for before.'

'Climbing?' Evie baulked, stumbling to a stop, as someone came out of the shop. 'Nate, I'm not—'

But the man who had come out of the shop was making a beeline for them. He smiled and held out a hand to Nate. He was quite short and was wearing a branded red polo shirt. Evie didn't know why, but she could imagine him on the set of *Alice in Wonderland*. Someone who worked for the Queen of Hearts maybe.

'You must be the journalist,' he said, in a brilliant West Country accent. So, working for the West Country Queen of Hearts then.

Nate nodded, shaking the man's hand. 'Nate Ritchie. And this is Evie.'

He barely spared her a glance. 'Great. I'm Tim. Well, come on in. I'll talk you through it all.' He started walking back to the shop, and Evie saw no choice but to follow them both. Folding her arms, stamping her foot and refusing to move wouldn't quite cut it, she thought. 'There are three different levels of the climbing wall – a bit like Go Ape, if you've ever…?'

Nate gave a sort of nod-shrug, whilst Evie bit her lip. Go Ape wasn't really her thing – not ever, but especially not since her diagnosis.

'Anyway,' Tim continued, 'we got everything ready for you before you got here, so we'll skip the shop – you can have a browse there later, if you like – and take you straight down. This is Ed,' he added, gesturing to a blond man who had come out of the shop exactly as they were passing. He also had a red polo shirt on – Queen of Hearts henchman, take two.

Ed, it seemed, also had the equipment, which Evie decided it was best not to look at. She wouldn't be doing it anyway. She *wouldn't*. 'Um, can I just—'

But Queen of Hearts A was talking again. 'So the theory is that there's a beginner one to get you started, a middle run and an advanced one for the challenge. You're attached to a line at all times, obviously, and there's one of our guys with you, if you need them. Really it's just a bit of fun on the beach; you know, an attraction for the tourists, but it's different because it's an outdoor climbing wall, so you're not in some indoor centre and you've got' – he gestured to the front door, and the coastline beyond it – 'waves in the background, the view from the cliffs, and all that.' He made a square with his hands, as if imagining it all on TV, or perhaps imagining what the article would look like.

Nate looked at Evie, who was lagging behind the three of them slightly. 'What do you reckon? Beginner, middle or advanced?'

Evie shook her head. 'I don't—'

But again she was talked over. 'Maybe she would do the beginner, and you can do the advanced? We want to encourage the girls to come too, of course!' He gave Evie a little salute, like that was somehow a compliment.

Nate raised his eyebrows, clearly thinking along the same sort of lines. She *wished* she was more the adventurous type. She wished she had a better, stronger body so that she could take the bloody beginner run and shove it up his—

She stumbled to a stop. There it was. And it wasn't a wall, it was a bloody cliff. A cliff with red, blue and green bits sticking out of the sides. Actually it looked a little tacky, if she was being totally honest – it slightly ruined the moodiness of the landscape. And really, why did anyone want to climb a damn cliff? What was the *point*?

Queen of Hearts B put down all the equipment – again she refused to look – and they both crouched down and started fumbling around with it. Evie took her opportunity and reached out to grab Nate's arm before he could join them. 'Nate, I can't do this,' she said. Why, *why* did she have to sound all pathetic and panicked? Why couldn't she just state it as a logical fact?

He looked down at her hand on his arm, then met her gaze. 'Why not?'

'Because…' She hated it, having to explain, having to highlight the problem. Her nerves spiked in a way that was painful. Why had he not remembered about her MS? Had he not thought she might struggle with this? Clearly he was one of those people who assumed that because she *looked* fine she wasn't struggling at all, when really—

She took a breath. 'My… my body doesn't *work* sometimes, it gets all stiff and I'm scared I won't be able to—'

135

'You guys ready?' Queen of Hearts A called over.

Evie took her hand away from Nate's arm and swallowed.

'You could try?' Nate asked. 'I get that you're scared, but surely you don't know until you try? If it's a problem, we can stop, get you down.' He turned his attention away from her, towards the Queen of Hearts duo. 'Tim? I'll do the beginner one too first, with Evie – I need to warm up a bit and, I'll be honest, the height of that one is a bit daunting.' He nodded towards the red side of the cliff, grinning. 'I've not done this in a while.'

'Of course, of course,' Tim said. 'We don't want to scare the guy who's giving us a good write-up!' He punched Nate on the arm, as Nate came up alongside him. 'But you will do the advanced one, yeah? Our red run? Only that's the one that we're most proud of and…'

'Course,' Nate said, 'just building up to it.'

Evie was still standing there, listening to the waves breaking against the shoreline behind her, the distant sound of children giggling. She resumed her stiff, halting walk when Tim and Nate turned to look at her expectantly.

Nate took off his jacket, slinging it over a nearby rock so that he was standing in a casual blue T-shirt. Evie couldn't help noticing his arm muscles – not all obvious and bulky like Will's, but definitely there, accentuated by a fading tan, almost *rippling* as he moved to put his harness on and— No, they were *not* rippling, who even said 'rippling'? Scarlett, she thought with a sad little smile; it was something Scarlett would have said.

Somehow, her protests being totally ignored by Men Who Thought They Knew Better, she was helped into a harness and then she was climbing. She was on the bloody cliff, her fate in the hands of a Queen of Hearts henchman below.

She heaved in a breath and started to climb. And actually, for the first bit, it was okay. The stiffness in her legs seemed to help keep her in place, and if she used her arms to pull herself up, she found she could do it. Badly, but still. Nate was keeping time with her and she could tell he was going deliberately slowly.

'What are you humming?' he asked, and Evie jerked slightly, stopping the hum.

'I didn't realize I was,' she said truthfully. But it was both calming her and pushing her on, the way music always did.

He gave her a sly grin. 'I can't be *sure*, but it sounded like the theme tune to *Pirates of the Caribbean*.'

She smiled a little, unable to feel embarrassed when she was clinging to a cliff. 'It was. I kind of love it,' she admitted. 'The soundtrack, not the movie. Though the movie's pretty good too.' And one of Scarlett's old favourites.

'I dressed up as Captain Jack Sparrow for Halloween once,' Nate said, reaching up to grab the next boulder, his breathing far more even than hers. 'But I couldn't quite master the mannerisms.'

Evie let out a huff that was almost a laugh, but now feeling too self-conscious to keep humming, she went quiet. She really *did* love that tune – it was the one with the violins, composed by Hans Zimmer, the one everyone

137

thinks about when they recall Johnny Depp in that film. She'd learned how to play it on her violin when she and Scarlett were teenagers, and Scarlett had been so delighted by it, she'd kept making Evie get out her violin and play it at parties.

About halfway up she nearly lost her grip on one of the green handle-things above her. Her heart spasmed, blood rushing to her head. She felt hot. Too hot. But she made herself take deep breaths. *Slowly*, she told herself.

Nate came to a stop next to her, leaning back on his harness so that he was basically hanging in mid-air, while she was gripping tightly onto the cliff. 'The view is pretty cool,' he said, nodding behind them. She shifted as much as she dared to, twisting her head to look. And it *was* cool. The sea was sparkling under the sunlight, the white frothy waves at the pebbly shore turning deeper and bluer the further out you looked. If you looked right out at the ocean, you could ignore the people on the beach below, the ice-cream truck further up and even the Queen of Hearts team beneath them. You could ignore it all and pretend you were here, alone. And for the first time since Scarlett had died, that aloneness did not feel terrifying. It did not feel lonely.

'There's something about the sea,' Evie murmured softly. 'It makes everything seem more peaceful.'

'Yeah. Though I used to go on family holidays to the seaside. Not here – Brighton mainly.' Nate was hanging off the side of the cliff so comfortably. How was he not terrified? 'We did the whole shebang: ice cream, fish and chips, obligatory swimming, no matter the weather. It was fun, but I wouldn't exactly call it *peaceful*,' he said with a little lopsided smile.

'You don't any more?'

'Not since my parents got divorced.' His smile faded at that and she saw the sadness creep into his brown eyes, a specific tone that she didn't think she'd seen on him before.

'My mum wasn't big into holidays,' she found herself saying. In fact Evie didn't think she'd ever been on a holiday with just her mum – they wouldn't know what to do with each other, cooped up in the same space for that long.

'And your dad?'

She shook her head, tried very hard *not* to look down. Objectively they weren't that high, but they *were* still on the side of a cliff. Her arms were starting to quiver. She wished she could shake them out, but didn't have the courage to do what Nate was doing and give the harness more of her body weight. 'My dad was never around – I've never actually met him.'

'Do you want to?'

She looked across at him. Not many people asked her that directly – at least not right away. They tended to express sympathy first, which, even after all this practice, Evie hadn't figured out how to respond to. Would it be like that with Scarlett now too? Would she ever figure out how to talk about it?

'No,' she said on a little sigh – an easy, truthful answer. 'I've never wanted to find him. He left, so what would be the point?' She glanced up, trying to see how much further they had to go. 'I mean, if he got in touch and wanted to meet, I wouldn't say no out of principle or anything – but that's kind of the point. It would be easy enough for him to find us, so I suppose I don't see the point of finding someone who doesn't want to be found.'

'That makes sense,' Nate said.

Evie blinked. 'It does?' Most people tried to convince her that she *should* want to meet him – like being linked biologically was more important than the people you met and made genuine connections with along the way.

'Yeah, I reckon so.'

With that, Nate started climbing again, and she pushed off, gritting her teeth against the dull pain. But after a few seconds her muscles spasmed, went rigid. Then they gave way and she let out a small scream as she slipped, hanging on with her arms.

'You're okay!' one of the guys called from below her, his voice deep and booming, loud enough to get through the blood pounding in her head. A sob escaped Evie as she clung onto the wall, but she managed to get one of her legs to obey her, to find a foothold again.

'It's all right, you can let go,' Nate said, his voice soothing and right next to her. 'He'll support you, you'll be okay.'

Evie squeezed her eyes shut and shook her head, still clinging.

'You're okay,' Nate said again.

'I'm not,' she said, embarrassingly close to crying.

'You are, look, you're—'

'I'm *not*, Nate.' And maybe because she'd already lost her temper with him – twice now – it was easy to snap, to let it out. 'I told you this would happen. I'm not strong enough. As in, it's not just that I'll be a bit sore or whatever: my body is *broken* and it's not strong enough for this.' She was breathing too quickly, couldn't stop. 'I shouldn't have come,' she muttered. 'I shouldn't have done this.' She let loose a glare at him, which Nate did not react to. Just kept looking at her out of calm eyes. 'I wouldn't have come if I'd known this was the plan.'

Which was probably why he didn't tell her. Damn it! Why, *why* had she let herself be poked into this, why had she not stood up for herself? She'd learned, hadn't she, not to overdo it? She knew her limitations. Wasn't that effectively what she'd said to Scarlett? *She* knew them, Nate didn't. And she couldn't expect him to, either – so she knew that her anger at him wasn't fair, that this was *her* fault, for caving, for not standing up to him, for—

He reached out, placed his hand over hers on the cliff. She jolted – she hadn't realized how close they were. She looked down at his hand; it was warm and dry and chalky on her skin, though hers must feel cold and clammy.

'I'm sorry,' he said. 'I don't know how it works – the MS thing.'

'I said I couldn't do it,' she repeated, but her voice was tired now.

'Yeah, but I thought it was because you were a bit scared, which is different.' She frowned at him and he smiled. 'Everyone's a bit scared of stuff, doesn't mean it's a reason not to do it. But look,' he said, talking over her when she opened her mouth to contradict him, 'we're nearly at the top.'

She glanced up, saw he was right. The ledge was there, almost close enough to touch. She looked down and swallowed. He gave her hand a friendly squeeze. 'See, now it's the height thing that's worrying you, and that's normal. Anyway you're here now, you might as well get to the top.'

She did get to the top. She pushed the last few feet up, because he was right: she *was* nearly there. And when she reached the ledge, and the green post to mark the end, she couldn't help it. She smiled – a smile that spread when Nate grinned over at her.

'Hey, look, we did it.'

She nodded. She was sore and could feel the tiredness setting in, and she was *angry* that her body had to work so much harder than other people's, but he was right – she'd done it. She blew out a breath and tentatively let go of the wall, put her weight on the harness.

'You totally nailed it,' Nate said with another smile.

'Well, I wouldn't go quite that far,' Evie said drily. But she *had* made it to the top. If she'd been given more of a choice, if he'd let her say no and taken that at face value, then there was absolutely no way she would even have tried. And maybe – just maybe – she might have lived to regret that.

Chapter Sixteen

Nate pulled up outside her flat and switched off the engine. He left the key in the ignition, so that the radio stayed on. Evie glanced at him, cleared her throat. 'Well, thanks for today, I guess.'

One corner of his mouth pulled up. 'You guess?'

She huffed out a breath that wasn't quite a laugh. 'I have kind of mixed feelings. No, but really, I'm glad I went. Even if... I know it didn't seem like it. And I know I... well, maybe I overreacted.' She felt herself flush. She shouldn't have lost her temper. What was it about him that brought it out in her?

'You didn't overreact. I should have paid more attention, I'm sorry.' He rubbed a hand across the back of his neck, and she knew it was a sign he was uncomfortable.

'No,' she said firmly. 'It's my responsibility – no one else's – to make sure I'm okay.'

Nate nodded slowly. 'How about we agree that we both could have done things a bit differently?'

Evie hesitated, then gave a little shrug. 'Okay, deal.' New territory, for her, to be talking about it like this, as if it were a compromise somehow, rather than all or nothing. She didn't know quite what to do with that yet.

The music changed on the radio and violins struck up, a lively tune, almost Irish-sounding. It wasn't a piece she recognized. It wasn't the piece that she and Scarlett had danced to, so many times; and then the singing started, and *their* piece did not have singing, it was instrumental alone. But still it was similar, the way the violins challenged each other. She looked away, out of the car window and into the dusky glow of London. Scarlett had loved it here. But now that she was gone, Evie found herself wondering how she'd bear it, staying here. It had seemed so obvious, when they'd moved, that it was the place for her too, because where better to follow your dreams than the capital? But really was there anything keeping her here? Her dream of playing for a living was now nothing but dust. She'd have to hand in her notice on the flat – there was no way she could afford to keep it, even if she'd wanted to continue living there on her own.

At least she had her job, she told herself firmly. A job she should be grateful for, given that she had an illness that would make some jobs difficult.

'You like music, I take it?' Nate asked, drawing Evie out of her own thoughts. She glanced at him, saw him looking at her hand, which was tapping out a rhythm on her leg, keeping time with the music. She stopped immediately, curling her fingers into her palm. She hadn't even realized she was doing it. And because it had been without intention, the tremor hadn't started.

'Doesn't everyone like music?' It was part of being human, after all. Music could evoke joy, sadness, wonder. Its effect could be instantaneous, or it could build. Some people she'd met said they were 'ambivalent' about music, which she thought was ridiculous. What would life be, without it? Didn't they realize that whenever they watched a film, it was the music in the background doing half of the work to make them feel what they felt?

'This kind of music then,' Nate said, gesturing towards the radio. 'Classical.'

'This isn't totally classical,' Evie said. 'It's almost more country. Though it's still beautiful,' she added, aware that some people thought she was a snob when she was pedantic about music. Which was another ridiculous thing – you didn't have to be a snob to love music, and they certainly wouldn't call her one if they saw the type of school she and Scarlett had gone to.

'So… yes?'

Evie shook her head. 'Sorry. Yes. I like music.' She cocked her head. 'Do you?'

'Course. But it's Taylor Swift all the way for me.'

Evie laughed – a small, quiet laugh, but a laugh still – and Nate grinned, his eyes creasing in the corners. For a moment their gazes met, held, and something deep inside her seemed to tremble, ever so slightly. Then she looked away and it was gone. She sighed. 'I better be going in.'

'Right. Er… Evie?' She looked over at him. 'Don't suppose I could use your loo, could I?' He gave a helpless little shrug. 'Long drive and all that.'

'Oh. Of course. Come on up.' She gave him a wry look. 'I mean, you already know which flat it is.' He didn't say anything, only gave her a sheepish smile at the reference to how he'd showed up without notice the last time.

He followed her into the block of flats and up the stairs. Evie heard it before she turned the corner. A few notes, carefully chosen.

Astrid was sitting there, wearing a hoodie again, frowning in concentration as her bow slid between her fingers and across the violin. 'Hello, Astrid,' Evie said as they got nearer to the top. 'We're making a habit of meeting like this.'

Astrid smiled up at Evie, who loved her smile, she decided right then. There was something so open, so uncomplicated about it.

'I'm practising again,' Astrid said, a little redundantly. She looked at Nate, who had come up alongside Evie on the stairs, gave him a quick scan up and down, as if sussing him out. Again, so open – she wasn't even *trying* to hide that's what she was doing. 'Is *this* your boyfriend?'

Evie decided not to react to the slight inflection on *this*. If Nate noticed, he didn't show it. 'No, he's…' She trailed off, glancing back at Nate. How, exactly, was she supposed to introduce him?

'A friend?' Nate gave her a quick grin, the one that she sensed was practised, that he'd used to get himself out of trouble before.

'An acquaintance,' Evie said decisively, then headed past Astrid to unlock her door.

'Dude, burn,' Astrid said behind her, getting to her feet and coming with Nate to stand behind Evie as she opened the door. It made Evie smile, though she kept it hidden. 'So, why are you here?' Astrid asked Nate, in that very direct way of hers.

'I, ah, just need the loo.'

'And what do you do?'

'I'm a journalist.'

'Really?' Her face went from suspicious to smiling in a flash. 'That's so cool,' she said earnestly.

'Yeah,' Nate agreed. 'I guess it's pretty cool.'

'I want to do that. Well, I want to play really, but that's unlikely to happen, or so everyone says, so being a journalist is, like, my backup. I want to dig up all the dirt on people, you know?'

Evie saw Nate struggling to squash a smile. 'Only specific journalists do that – you might be better being a private detective or something.' Astrid opened her mouth. 'I don't know anything about that, though,' Nate said quickly.

Evie stepped inside the flat and raised her eyebrows when Astrid followed Nate inside. 'Astrid, are you supposed to be—' But she didn't get to finish.

'Oh. My. God. Is that yours?' Astrid's brown eyes literally seemed to *glow* as she stepped towards the corner of the room.

Evie felt herself go stiff as Nate followed Astrid's gaze towards it. Her violin, propped against the small desk.

She'd taken it out last night. Taken it out and looked at it, and tried to remember what it had felt like, when she was still so sure that music would be in her life – her career – somehow. She hadn't been able to put it away, so there it was, in the corner of the room. It looked so lonely, she thought then, half hidden in the shadows. Almost sorrowful. Violins were made to be played, and this one…

well, it had lost its purpose when she had lost hers. And right then she felt such a strong pang for it that she brought her hand to her chest and rested it there.

Astrid turned to her, looking at her questioningly.

'Yes,' Evie said, trying to keep her voice even. Mine.'

'I knew it!' Astrid stepped towards it, hands clasped in front of her. 'You play.'

'I played. Past tense.' She sensed Nate watching her now, but refused to return the look. It was none of his business.

'I would give *anything* for something like this,' Astrid said, standing right over the violin now. She reached out as if to touch it, then snatched her fingers back and looked over her shoulder guiltily at Evie.

Evie smiled, trying to soothe away the snap. 'You can say hello, if you like. She probably misses the company.'

Astrid reached out one finger to touch the violin, while Nate gave Evie a look. 'She?' he asked, and Evie waved a hand.

'All the best things are female,' she said.

Nate nodded. 'I suppose I'd agree with that.'

Astrid brought her hand back, then turned round and made a show of looking around the flat. 'This place is, like, the same size as mine and Mum's.'

Evie raised her eyebrows. 'I suppose that would make sense – same building and all.'

'Suppose so. So you live here alone?' She gave Nate a shady look, and Evie saw Nate catch the smile before it filled his face. She couldn't smile, though. Alone. There was that word again. And suddenly the absence of Scarlett pressed down on her, in a way that was overwhelming.

She felt Nate watching her as he spoke. 'Hey, Astrid, why don't we—'

But he was cut off by a shriek across the hallway. 'Anna!' Astrid winced. 'Anna, I swear to God if you're—'

Astrid crossed to Evie's still-open doorway and opened it wider to show a woman, in her late thirties maybe, brilliantly curvy with dark wavy hair, looking a little frantic, about to start down the stairs.

'I'm here, Mum.' The woman spun round to Astrid – *Anna?* – and rested a hand at the base of her throat.

'What the hell are you playing at? Who are these people?' She gave Nate and Evie a suspicious look, before focusing back on her daughter.

'They're my friends,' Astrid said and it sounded so easy, to phrase it like that. A few words exchanged and – bam!, friends, no questions asked. 'Better go,' Astrid said to Evie and Nate, scurrying to the door.

But Evie took a step after her. 'Anna?' She looked back. 'You said your name was—'

'Well, I don't *like* Anna, so I'm trying out something new. See ya!' She stepped out, shut the door behind her, though it didn't block out the sound of her mother, lecturing her about stranger-danger.

'She's not a stranger, Mum, she's our neighbour and she's cool.'

Evie stared at the closed door for a moment, wondering whether to be offended or worried that Astrid – Anna – had lied so easily about her name. She turned to Nate, who was still hovering there. 'The loo's down the hallway,' she said. 'Last door on the right.'

'Okay. Thanks.'

She sank onto the little red sofa once he was gone. God, she needed to sleep. It came on like this – sudden and all-encompassing. Today had been a stretch, so it was hardly surprising, but still.

She didn't notice Nate coming back in until he spoke behind her. 'Can I make you a cup of tea or something?' She turned and blinked at him.

'Okay,' she said, aware that her voice had gone a bit numb again. She wanted him to leave really, so that she could crash, but the way he was watching her in that uncertain way made her think he needed to do something, so she'd let him make her a cup of tea and then she'd send him on his way.

He didn't ask her where everything was, but set about rummaging around her kitchen, and she was reminded, with a sharp little stab, of Will, not that long ago. She heard Nate flick the kettle on, then the movement stopped.

There was a beat of silence and then, 'What's this?'

She twisted to look from the sofa, and he held up a piece of paper for her to see. Her heart spasmed. She'd left it out. She'd found it in Scarlett's folder on her desk, but she hadn't been able to bring herself to call Jason about it yet – hadn't been able to give it up.

It was a dress. Multiple sketches of the same dress: Scarlett in the early stages of a design. It was long, hanging sleek to the floor, tight and loose in different places, sweeping low across the back. And in the centre of the page was a drawing of a woman wearing the dress – a woman who was unmistakably Evie. Drawn with a softness about her that she wasn't sure she still had. There were labels around the edges, so although it wasn't coloured, Evie knew what Scarlett was intending – she wanted it to be green. She had a flash, of the two of them on the beach in Crete.

I can't wait to be one of the first ones to buy an original Scarlett Henderson.

I'll make it something green, just for you.

'Scarlett designed it. Or she drew it, I suppose – she was going to design it, to make it, I think.' Evie blew out a breath, tore her gaze away from the charcoal drawing. 'I think she was going to make it for me for my thirtieth. It's not until August, but she said a while back that she was going to make me something epic, and I think… I think that was it.'

He looked back at the drawing, and Evie couldn't read his expression. 'I think you're right,' he said eventually and set the drawing down.

The kettle clicked off and Nate filled two mugs, set one down on the coffee table in front of her. 'Can I get you anything else?' She shook her head. 'Water?' he pressed. 'Food? Do you *have* any food I can make you?'

'I'm not sure.' She couldn't remember when she'd last been shopping. She moved her arm to pick up her tea, but the tremor started, so she dropped her hand.

Without saying anything, Nate grabbed the mug off the table, set it in her lap, where she could wrap her hands around it.

'Thanks,' she said on a sigh. Usually she'd feel embarrassed that she needed someone to help her with such a small task, but she didn't have the energy.

'It doesn't always seem to be there,' he said, a little hesitantly.

She flexed her fingers against the mug. 'It's the most constant symptom. That and the tiredness, though that can come and go. But yeah, there are times when it's worse.' She looked up at him. 'You can go. Honestly. I can sort myself out – I'll order something in or…'

He hesitated, like he might protest, and she got it: she knew how she looked. But really the best thing she could do for herself right now was sleep. Thankfully he seemed to pick up on that and nodded, before heading back to the kitchen. She heard him washing up his mug, placing it on the draining board. Such a small action, but a considerate one.

Maybe that's why the next words came out. 'It's her birthday tomorrow.' She felt, rather than saw, him look over her, and kept her gaze on her mug as she continued. 'Scarlett would have been thirty tomorrow.'

It hung between them. The fact that she wasn't there because she'd stopped to help him. It wasn't why she was telling him – but it didn't stop it from being true.

'I was going to take her out,' Evie said. 'She wasn't really looking forward to it – her birthday. She didn't want to turn thirty.' The thought twisted something inside her: Scarlett hadn't wanted to turn thirty, hadn't wanted to leave her twenties behind. And she hadn't. She would be eternally twenty-nine. Evie took a breath, tried to allow the

152

grief to roll through her, in the way it needed to. 'So me and her mum, we were going to organize this big party for next weekend, but on the actual day I was going to take her to this restaurant she'd always wanted to go to – they play music, and we could dance and drink champagne and…' She clutched her mug tighter between her fingers. 'It's stupid, to think about it now.'

'It's not stupid,' Nate said immediately. 'Which restaurant?'

She named it and glanced over to him, to see him standing at the kitchen counter, by the drawing – and by the unopened letter of Scarlett's – nodding.

'I'll take you,' he said, a little abruptly.

'What?'

He rubbed a hand across the back of his neck – one of his tells. 'If you're not doing anything tomorrow… I mean, do you? Have plans? Tomorrow?'

She hesitated. Then shook her head – what was the point in lying? 'No. But I don't think I could… It would feel wrong, to go there without her.'

'Somewhere else then. I'll take you somewhere else. We can celebrate her, together.'

'I don't know,' Evie said slowly. Celebrating Scarlett's birthday with the man who was inadvertently the cause of her death: wasn't there something horribly wrong with that? Still, his words bounced around her mind. *Celebrate her.* Something in her stirred at it. Because Scarlett, with all her life and energy, she'd have *wanted* to be celebrated, wouldn't she?

'Well, text me. If you want to. No pressure.'

She looked up, nodded. 'Thank you.'

'I'll, er, let myself out.'

He moved towards the door and she watched him. Such an easy, confident stride. 'Nate?'

He jolted, looked back at her almost like he thought he was about to be told off. 'Yeah?'

'I… Thank you. For today.'

He smiled at her – really smiled in a way that looked so genuine. And she couldn't help it. She felt glad, just for a moment, that she was the one making him smile like that.

Chapter Seventeen

She did it! Evie actually climbed that wall. If it had been me asking her to do it, I know she would have flat out refused. But maybe that's because we know each other so well – you can say no to those closest to you, can't you? That said, there is a part of me that knows I wouldn't have pushed, like Nate did. That knows I probably wouldn't even have tried to make her do something like that, because I thought I knew exactly what her answer would be.

I feel a rush of guilt at that. When did I start giving up on my best friend?

I didn't, I tell myself firmly. Don't the brochures, which are still hidden in the kitchen drawer, prove that I hadn't given up on her? But maybe I could have tried harder. I could have tried to find that balance between encouraging Evie to do a little more and accepting that she can't do some things, instead of letting her retreat completely. I was always telling her not to let her illness define her, but perhaps I was starting to do that too – thinking of her illness before thinking of her. What does it say that Nate already seems to be figuring out the line I couldn't, without even trying?

He found my drawing. He took a photo of it – what is that about? I'm not sure I like that. Why does he need a photo of it?

More important, though, this means that *Evie* found it – how did I miss that? It's just sitting there, on the side. Next to my letter.

She's right: I did want the dress to be hers. And seeing her talking about it, I realize I don't want her to give the design to Jason. I want her to keep it, to know that I was thinking of her as I drew it. But I know, as Nate shuts the door, leaving her alone for the night, that the dress is not the thing playing on her mind right now.

My thirtieth. I haven't been clocking the time passing, the way I would if I were alive, and the fact that it is my birthday *tomorrow* comes as a bit of a shock: 15 June. I've always loved that my birthday was right in the middle of June – it felt special, somehow. Evie and I, both summer babies. Now, though, the date means it's been two months since I died. Two months stuck like this. Is that even possible? Will it be endless, watching other people's lives play out, revisiting memories that have stuck with me, one way or another? As if in answer, I find myself back on the pavement, watching a man on a red bike as he— *No.* I block out the image, wrench myself away from it. I'm not ready to do it all again.

Instead I think of my last birthday, spent with Jason, just the two of us. He took me away for the night, to some fancy hotel in Brighton overlooking the sea – a nicer beach, in my opinion, than the one Evie described as *peaceful* today. It was the first birthday I'd spent not with Evie, though we celebrated later, at the weekend, and I'd taken it as a mark of adulthood somehow – spending my birthday with a 'significant other' rather than with my friend. *Significant Other.* Did I ever have the right to call him that?

I don't go back to that memory now, though. I'm surprised to find myself instead at the local pub, where Evie used to waitress as a teenager, the yeasty smell of beer in the air. It's my twenty-first and I'm standing with my back to Evie in the middle of a circle of all our friends, and if the way my body feels like it's swaying slightly is anything to go by, then I'm well on my way to being pissed. I don't remember much about my twenty-first, other than general dancing and excitement – so why am I here?

We're playing Back-to-Back. I don't know the official name of the game, but that's what we called it – where you stand back-to-back with someone else, and people on the outside of the circle ask questions like, 'Who is the more intelligent?' and if you think it's you, then you have to drink. If both of you drink – or neither – then you're out. But the thing is: Evie and I are excellent at this game. We know each other too well, so we're pretty unbeatable – because even if we don't agree, we know what the *other* one will think. Who is the bravest? Me. Who is the more polite? Evie. Who is the most likely to end up in prison? Me. Who is the grumpiest? Also me. Who can hold their alcohol better? Evie, but only because she's taller. Who is the prettiest? I know Evie will say me to this, so I drink – because that's how you win the game. Who has the best eyes? At this, I frown. My eyes are my best feature, I know – I spent ages learning which eye make-up to use to complement the shade of blue exactly, and I make sure that whenever I talk to someone I look at them directly, so that they clock my eyes. But Evie has great eyes too. All green and mermaid-like. She doesn't necessarily *use* them like I do, but when she looks at you directly… well, let's just say they hit you. It's something we bonded over, when we first met: how neither of us had *common* (I'm pretty sure we'd only recently learned that word in that context) brown eyes.

Someone on the outskirts of the circle – Sasha, one of my friends from uni – laughs. 'Finally! Both of you drink!' Evie and I face each other and grin.

'To having great eyes,' I say, and we cheers our rosé. It's gross – *why* are we drinking this?

Twenty-one. It feels so young. Why do people make a big deal about twenty-one? It doesn't really mean anything any more, does it? But somehow it *felt* like a big deal, like I was stepping into adulthood somehow.

I move back into the circle, and two of my and Evie's school friends step into the middle. Across the circle I catch Jake, one of the guys from Evie's university, looking at me. We've been dancing around this for a while now, having met in Manchester a few weeks ago on a night out. Later on we'll have awkward, fumbling, drunk sex and will go on to date for a total of four months, but at the time I thought he was the most gorgeous thing I'd ever seen, all tall, dark and handsome with big-muscled shoulders and… well, clearly I have a type, don't I?

I excuse myself from the circle, desperate for a wee. On the way back from the loo I pass my parents in the corner of the pub, separate from the rest of us. They've rented the whole place out. Earlier that night it had been even busier, some of my parents' friends coming too, but the crowd has thinned as the night wore on.

'I'm not saying right now,' my dad is muttering, in a hushed tone that isn't quite hushed enough. 'I'm just saying we should have a conversation with her about—'

'Not *now*, Graham. It's our baby girl's twenty-first, can't you leave it for one night?'

'Leave what?' I pipe up as I cross to their table, the alcohol making me slightly more invasive – and perhaps more slurry – than I would usually be.

'Nothing, love.' Mum smiles up at me brightly, but I can see it's an effort.

'Who were you going to have a conversation with?' I press. 'Me?'

Dad shakes his head. 'Don't worry about it, Lettie.' Lettie, the name he used for me when I was little. It sends a fresh pang through me as I think of my parents, sleeping in different rooms, each alone in their grief. God, I want to cry. I want to cry but I can't, because the me of the past has no reason for tears.

I hesitate, but Mum gestures to the other side of the pub. 'Go, entertain your friends. You are the birthday girl, after all.' She gives me a wink. Aha! Maybe that's where I got it from.

It doesn't take long, once I'm back with the group, for Jake to come and stand next to me. 'Drink?' he asks.

'Sure.' I follow him to the bar and he orders me another rosé. As he hands it to me, his hand grazes mine, lingers for a moment and I lift my gaze to his.

'I've got my own room, in the Airbnb,' he says, and there is a hint of a blush there that I can't help finding endearing.

'Do you now?' I say, smiling coyly. A bunch of my uni friends came down together, making a weekend of it. 'What's it like? The place?'

He shrugs. 'It's all right.' I raise my eyebrows and he cottons on, speaking quickly. 'I mean, it's nice. Really nice. You should see it.'

I tap my glass, as if thinking about it. 'Do you have wine?'

He grins. 'We've got white, in the fridge.'

'That'll do, I suppose.'

He goes to get my coat, practically skipping, and I find Evie. 'So-o-o-o, I think I'm going to go and have sex with Jake.'

Evie laughs, a little high-pitched, then gives me a look. She was never quite as brazen as me about all that. 'Seriously?'

I grin at her. 'Seriously.'

'Oh. So you're leaving? Now?' I can see it then, the flash of hurt across her face, which she does her best to cover up. I don't think the me in the past noticed, though.

'Yep.' I down the rest of my wine, set the empty glass on the nearest table. 'That's okay, right?'

'Yes, of course. It's your party. Go. Before the rest of them follow.'

I grin again. 'That's the plan. You'll still have fun though, right, without me? Loads of people are still here.'

'Course. We might have *more* fun without you here, in fact.'

I laugh, bump my shoulder against hers. 'As if.'

'Oh, it was all part of the master plan,' she says, nodding serenely. 'I thought it all through, positioned Jake just right. In fact I'm a bit disappointed it took so long.'

I prod her in the ribs – she's trying to make light of it, I know, so that I don't feel bad about it. Jake comes up next to me, shoots Evie a slightly guilty look. He was her friend, before he became my crush.

'Ready?' he asks, and I nod.

As for Evie, she'd broken up with her first boyfriend a few months ago. Some boring dude she'd met who'd studied Computer Science. That's unfair. I'm sure there are interesting people who study Computer Science – he just wasn't one of them. What was his name again? Roland? Or Ronald? Seriously, who's called Ronald? Who *introduces* themselves as Ronald, and not Ron? I'm pretty sure it was Roland actually, but still. I think I'd been full of grand plans to set Evie up with someone at my party, but clearly I have abandoned that idea.

Jake takes my hand as we leave the pub, and I don't even look back over my shoulder. Don't say goodbye to the rest of my friends, my parents. Who was I, that I could do that? They'd all come out for me, and I'd left because of this *boy*. I'd justified those moments to myself, claiming that you had to prioritize certain things if you were ever going to find the right man. And at that moment maybe I really believed that was Jake.

So I leave them all, leave Evie. She'll laugh about it the next day, tease me about Jake, and she'll be lovely to him, like she always was with my boyfriends. I don't think she and Jake stayed friends after I broke up with him, because he 'didn't want the reminder' of me. I didn't really think of him again, after that. On to London, to bigger and better things. Another man in my desperate search to find 'The One' – a search I'm not sure I ever accomplished.

Chapter Eighteen

Evie almost let her phone ring out when she saw it was her mum calling. But she'd been finding reasons not to call her for weeks now and she knew the time had come. So she picked the phone up off the kitchen counter, where she'd been considering pouring herself a glass of the cheap white wine that she'd stored in the fridge. It was after midday, after all. On Scarlett's birthday.

'Hi, Mum.'

'Evelyn! Nice to hear your voice at last.' There was a subtle trace of accusation in her voice, one that Evie was more than used to.

'Sorry,' she said automatically. 'I've been…' She wanted to say *busy*, but of course Ruth was hardly going to believe that.

'Well, anyway,' her mum said briskly, negating the need for Evie to find a word to fill the gap. 'How are you?'

'I'm all right, I guess.'

'Hmm. Have you been eating? You looked thin, last time I saw you.' At the funeral. The last time they'd seen each other was at Scarlett's funeral, though neither of them said that.

'Yes, Mum, I've been eating,' Evie said, knowing it was easier not to argue.

'Good, because I read something the other day about how if you don't eat properly in your thirties, you'll end up really struggling once you hit the menopause. Plays havoc with your hormones apparently.'

'Well, good thing I'm not in my thirties then.' Evie took her tea and crossed to the sofa, one hand holding her phone to her ear.

'A few months is hardly something to haggle over – it's something to think about, Eve.'

Eve. She hated that.

'And where, exactly, did you read this?'

'Oh, I don't know. One of those blogs, you know.'

'A reliable source of information, I'm sure.' Evie crossed her legs underneath her on the sofa, perched her tea on her knee.

'Well, I wish I'd paid more attention to that kind of thing when *I* was in my thirties – the menopause is proving hell, I tell you. But then again, I had a teenage girl to worry about and you were so fussy, you only wanted to eat pasta all the time, so what was I supposed to do?'

Evie felt her temples throb. That was, what: a minute? Maybe two? Two whole minutes before her mum had brought up how, in one way or another, having Evie had had a negative impact on her life. 'I'm pretty sure *you* were the one who banned fruit from the house for three months, if I remember rightly.'

'Do you not remember the spider incident, Eve?' Her mum's voice had risen a fraction. 'There was a *reason* not to eat fruit – who knows what kind of thing we might have had in the house, otherwise.' She was referring to the fact that someone had been bitten by a spider and ended up dying, after the spider had hidden away in a box of pineapples from somewhere or other. Evie remembered Ruth skirting the fruit aisle in the supermarket for months, giving the pineapples deeply suspicious looks.

'So apples from England were a big danger, were they?'

'There is no telling where the fruit comes from these days, Evelyn. They're importing everything, left, right and centre.'

'If you say so.' She didn't know why she still tried to contradict her – it took more effort than it was worth.

'Which reminds me, I must book an appointment with Dr Hennessy.' As far as Evie could gather, Ruth changed doctors about every three months, claiming that she wasn't being listened to; every time she mentioned her doctor, it was a different name. Evie didn't ask – she didn't want to encourage her – but that didn't stop Ruth. 'I've been feeling a bit of tingling in my feet recently, and I know that can be a sign of diabetes.'

Evie sighed. 'It'll just be pins and needles, Mum.' And she'd know, wouldn't she? Tingling pain was something you had to expect when you had MS.

'Hmm, well, you *say* that, but I read something recently that stated all the pesticides we're consuming – you know, on all the *apples* you think are so safe – are leading to a massive rise in diabetes. Besides, it doesn't hurt to get it checked out, does it?'

Evie closed her eyes briefly, temples throbbing again. *It doesn't hurt to get checked out, does it?* It was what Scarlett had said – or a version of it – when Evie had started experiencing her first symptoms. Tiredness, blurred vision. An odd, sharp pain around her middle, striking with seemingly no warning. But she'd brushed it off. Being tired wasn't *serious*. She didn't want to be a nuisance to the NHS and bother them with something so minor. Not like her mum, who constantly took up the doctor's time with her hypochondriac tendencies.

She was trying not to resent her mother for it. Really she was. Scarlett had always said that one of the best things about Evie was the fact that she never held a grudge, and she wanted it to be true in this case too. But that didn't stop it creeping in, when her defences were low. Like smoke, filling in the gaps in her mind.

'Anyway, that's not the point,' her mum said.

'No?'

'No. I rang because… because I know it's Scarlett's birthday today.'

A jolt ran through Evie, both at Scarlett's name and the fact that Ruth had remembered. She hadn't thought she would. Hadn't even realized her mum knew when Scarlett's birthday was.

Ruth seemed to be waiting for her to acknowledge that. 'It is,' she said eventually, not knowing what else to say.

'Well, I wanted to see how you were doing, that was all. If you needed anything. Or maybe – you could come and spend the day with me?' That was the second time she'd offered this now, since Scarlett had died. She'd never offered before, the whole time Evie had been in London. Had acted glad, really, that Evie was gone, kept making comments about how nice it was to have the space. She'd already made Evie's old bedroom into a 'health room', which basically consisted of four yoga mats and a big bouncy ball, as far as Evie could tell.

'I…' Evie felt her throat close, swallowed to try and alleviate it. 'I think I'd rather spend it alone.' Not entirely true. 'But thank you.'

'Yes, well.' Her mum cleared her throat and Evie could tell that she, too, was feeling awkward, unsure of how to negotiate unfamiliar territory. 'Well,' she repeated. 'I sent some flowers, to Mel and Graham today.'

Evie sat more upright. 'You did?' Why hadn't she thought to do that? She'd wondered whether to call them – was still wondering that in fact, and was planning to make the decision after her first glass of wine. But flowers… It should have been her, not her mum, thinking of that.

'Yes. Do you think that's okay? I said they were from both of us.' And Mel would assume, Evie knew, that *Evie* had been the one to send them and added Ruth's name to be nice. And her mum must have known that, surely – because Evie had a far better relationship with Mel than she did, Ruth being jealous of Mel for so many reasons.

'I think it's a lovely gesture, Mum.' And she meant it. She imagined the flowers might make Mel cry, when she saw them. But at least she'd know that other people were thinking about Scarlett on her birthday.

'Yes, well, I can't imagine what she's going through. To lose a daughter like that…' She trailed off, and Evie's heart stuttered. She and her mum had never been close. Never. They never said *I love you* to one another, didn't chat or go to get their nails done or drink wine together. They didn't even have big shouting matches. They were just sort of… in each other's lives. And she'd always got the impression that her mum would rather never have got pregnant, never gone through with it.

There was a knock at Evie's front door. Considering that she had gone out of her way to be picky about who she spent her time with since her diagnosis – maybe a bit *too* picky, if she was being totally honest with herself – she seemed to be getting a lot of visitors recently.

'There's someone here, Mum, so I've got to go, sorry.' She was glad of the excuse to say goodbye, not to string out the conversation. Then she immediately felt guilty.

'Okay. Well, if you need me, then you know where I am.'

'I do.' She hesitated. *To lose a daughter like that…* 'Thank you for calling. Really. It means a lot, that you thought of Scarlett. Of me.'

'Of course.' There was a pause. 'And I do, you know.'

'Do what?'

'Think of you. Even if I don't always… You're my daughter, Evelyn.'

There was another knock and, after hanging up, Evie dropped her phone on the sofa, went to answer it. She raised her eyebrows when she saw who it was. 'Anna.'

'Astrid,' she corrected. 'I like Astrid better.'

Evie shrugged. 'Fair enough. Astrid, then. What's up?'

'I was wondering...' She looked down at the frayed carpet in front of Evie's door. 'Is it cool if I hang out with you for a bit?' She peeked up at Evie.

'Um... Hang out?'

'Yeah, because my mum is going out for the afternoon – something to do with my dad, even though it is a Sunday, can you believe it? But she says she's working all week and can't do it then, and she won't let me come along. She won't say why, but I'm pretty sure it's something to do with the divorce, and my dad, like, doesn't want me there or whatever, but she's said that if she's going out, I'm not allowed to be by myself, which is *totally* ridiculous because I'm thirteen and definitely able to spend a few hours on my own.' Astrid – if she wanted to be called that, then fine by Evie – gulped in a huge breath, not having paused through the whole rant.

'Um...' Evie said again, thinking of the wine waiting for her in the fridge.

'Please,' Astrid said, looking directly at her then. 'I don't have anyone else to ask, and I do *not* want a babysitter. Can you even imagine?'

'All right,' Evie said eventually. It was the last bit that got her. *I don't have anyone else to ask.*

Astrid beamed. 'Cool. I'll go tell Mum.' She bounded across the corridor to her own flat, while Evie hovered uncertainly.

It didn't take long for Astrid's mum to open the door and give Evie a speculative look from her side of the corridor. 'Are you sure this is okay?'

Evie nodded. 'Do you know how long you'll be?'

The woman wrinkled her nose. 'About three hours, I think.'

So she'd have her place to herself again by early evening, at least.

'Okay. Sure.'

'Thank you. I'm Julie, by the way. And I hear you're Evie.'

'I am indeed.'

Astrid appeared again then, clutching a plain black rucksack. 'Bye, Mum.' She barely had to stand on tiptoes to give her mother a kiss.

'Um… Good luck?' Evie said, and Julie nodded.

'Anna has my number, if anything happens.'

'Right, okay.' Was she even qualified to look after a teenager? Surely it was pretty straightforward – surely you just left them to their own devices?

When Evie shut the door behind her and turned round, Astrid was grinning, holding up a box of hair dye. Evie baulked, though she tried to hide it. 'Is that for you or me?'

'Me, duh.'

Evie held out a hand for the box. 'You want to go black, huh?'

'Yep. Like, ebony.'

Evie handed the box back. 'I don't think that's such a good idea. You don't want me to get in trouble with your mum, do you?'

'Whatever – she won't care. Besides, it's not her hair. I also want it short. Like, all the way cropped, you know?'

Evie narrowed her eyes. 'I am *not* cutting your hair.'

'Sure you are,' Astrid said easily. 'It's not hard.'

'How would you know? Cut a lot of hair, do you?'

She flapped a hand. 'I'm not, like, fussy. I just want to try it out. Hey, can I have a glass of water? You don't have any Coke, do you?'

'Yes, and no.' Evie headed to the kitchen, got out a glass for Astrid, filled it up. Turned to see Astrid looking at the little whiteboard on the fridge.

'Who's the message from? I thought you said you lived alone.'

Evie hesitated. 'My best friend wrote it. She lived here, with me.' She blew out a breath. 'She died. Two months ago.'

Astrid looked at her, wide-eyed. 'Oh.'

'Yeah. Today is her birthday. Or was,' she said on a sigh. 'I don't know which.'

And then, taking Evie completely by surprise, so much so that she nearly jumped, Astrid put her water down on the counter, crossed to Evie and hugged her, her skinny little arms coming around Evie's waist, her head resting on Evie's chest. Evie stood awkwardly for a moment before she let out a breath and hugged her arms around Astrid's shoulders.

'I don't, like, know what to say,' Astrid muttered, her voice a little muffled.

'That's okay. I don't know what to say, either.'

'Was she cool? I bet she was cool.'

'Yeah,' Evie said, her throat clogging. 'Yeah, she was cool.'

Astrid nodded as she pulled back. 'What are you doing for her today?' Evie frowned. 'It's her birthday, right? If I was dead, I reckon I'd want everyone to have a big party or something.' She made a face. 'Not that I have any friends this side of London *to* have a party with. Though I've joined the orchestra,' she added as an afterthought.

'You have? That's great.'

'Yeah. There's this one other girl in it that plays the cello. She's pretty good, I guess.' Competition or a potential friend? Evie wondered. 'There's this end-of-year concert coming up. They're doing this group performance and some people get solos. But I don't know if I'm going to do it. I don't know if I'm, like, good enough.'

'Maybe you won't know until you try?'

'Yeah, maybe.' She shook her head. 'Anyway, not the point. Your friend – you should do something for your friend. What did she like?'

Evie pulled a hand through her hair. Was she really having this conversation with a thirteen-year-old? Yes, she decided. Yes, she was. 'Clothes,' she said, smiling a little. 'Clothes, and going out, and dancing. And champagne. And laughing,' she added, huffing out a little laugh.

'Well, then,' Astrid said contemplatively. 'You should, like, go out and dance and laugh then.'

Nate's face flashed in Evie's mind again – those deep-brown eyes, messy hair, easy grin. His offer to spend Scarlett's birthday with her.

Wrong, she told herself.

She saw her phone flash on the sofa, crossed to it. A WhatsApp from Will, popping up at the top of her screen. Her stomach pulsed, ever so slightly.

Hope you're doing okay today. Miss you. Xx

'Is that from that guy?' Astrid piped up.

'Which guy?' Evie asked automatically, before she realized how it sounded.

'The hot one.'

Evie looked over at her.

'The journalist,' Astrid qualified.

Evie cocked her head, tried for a smile. 'You think he's hot?'

Astrid, though, did not blush. 'Sure, if you're into that sort of thing.'

'What sort of thing?' Evie wiggled her eyebrows, tried for jokey. 'Old men?' Was *she* old, to Astrid?

At this Astrid did blush, just a little. 'Something like that,' she said, not meeting Evie's gaze.

'Well, it's not from Nate, no.' Did it say something that she'd rather it *had* been from Nate than from Will? Well, she supposed it said that she shouldn't sleep with Will again, for one thing. Not that she would. And actually, thinking about that caused something hot to stir in her stomach. She shouldn't have been so pathetic, so pliable. But *he* shouldn't have come round like that, he shouldn't be treating her like this. Shouldn't have treated her like it in the first bloody place. It wasn't news, really. But it just… hit her, the fact of it.

Astrid was watching Evie while shifting from foot to foot. 'Are you okay?'

Evie blew out a breath. 'Sorry, yeah. So, hair dye then?' Astrid grinned.

And fine, Evie would help her dye her hair. Because do you know what: life was too bloody short, wasn't it? So if Astrid wanted her hair black and short, then why the hell not? The slight snag came when Evie tried to use the kitchen scissors to cut Astrid's hair – and the tremor kicked in, making her cut all wonky. But Astrid looked in the mirror while Evie was apologizing, looking down at the chunks of hair on her bathroom floor in horror, and she grinned again.

'I *love* it,' she said. 'It's, like, totally unique.' She made Evie laugh.

And when Julie came to pick Astrid up, thanking Evie profusely and only looking mildly put out by her daughter's new hair, Evie got out her phone and sent a text.

If you're still up for it, I'd love to go out tonight.

Because they were both right – Nate and Astrid. Scarlett didn't deserve to have Evie sitting around, crying into her wine. She deserved to be mourned, yes. But she also deserved to be *celebrated*.

Chapter Nineteen

Evie tried not to feel self-conscious as the doorman showed her through the hotel – with its grand mirrors and piano – and into the bar. The Rivoli Bar, at the Ritz.

It wasn't where she'd been planning to take Scarlett – they'd never have been able to afford it – but she'd let Nate decide. She wasn't sure whether she was dressed right; what was right, for one of the fanciest hotels in London? She was wearing one of her best dresses, one that was Scarlett Henderson-approved. It wasn't glitzy – she didn't pull off glitzy – but Scarlett had told her that was fine; she was more *classy*, apparently. It was black on top, high-necked, then fanned out into a long pleated skirt, which was pink and grey and black, all different shapes.

Nate was sitting at the bar itself, rather than at one of the tables in the relatively small, intimate space, but he stood up when he saw her. He'd dressed up too, wearing black trousers, a pale-blue shirt and a black jacket – one that showed off his muscles, which she couldn't help but notice. He'd even shaved for the occasion, though she thought she might like the stubble better.

'I couldn't get us a table in the main restaurant,' Nate said, a little apologetically, as she approached. Evie shook her head, hoping that expressed that he didn't need to apologize, as she looked around her, taking it all in. The whole bar had a kind of golden glow to it – the very floor seeming illuminated beneath them. The walls were in a sleek wooden style, and chandeliers hung from the ceiling, an automatic sign of glamour. The lighting was exactly right: nothing too bright, too overbearing. Behind the bar the bottles were all lit up – it was amazing, wasn't it, how you could make a bottle of vodka look so much better with the right lighting? There were people seated in armchairs around them – they had leopard-print armchairs; seriously, what kind of place could get away with that and still look classy?

This was the part of London Evie only really got glimpses of, though she was always aware that there were people all around her living in *this* London, while she was living in hers. Scarlett had straddled the two sides of the city much more, attending parties, meeting people who moved in this world, drinking at champagne bars until closing.

Evie was grateful for her height as she manoeuvred herself onto the tall, high-backed wooden bar stool semi-gracefully. She imagined Scarlett on one next to them, her legs dangling because she was so short. The image made her want to smile, though the urge faded as her throat closed. Laugh or cry? Memories of Scarlett seemed to be skirting that edge more and more, recently.

When the bartender came over, Nate ordered two glasses of champagne. Evie bit her lip as she looked at the prices on the menu in front of her. 'Don't worry,' he said, and Evie glanced over to him. 'I know a guy here, I'll sort it.'

Of course he did. He was a journalist, writing about the best tourist destinations all round the world. He was one of those who moved adjacent to the glamour of London, even though he didn't live here.

The bartender brought over two glasses of champagne, in those fancy 1920s glasses rather than flutes, and placed a bowl of nuts and those posh crunchy snacks in between them too. Evie lifted her glass, and Nate clinked his against it. 'To Scarlett,' he said softly.

Evie took a moment, allowed the full force of missing her friend to wash through her. Then she took a sip. 'Oh my God,' she breathed. 'This is literally the best glass of champagne I've ever had. Maybe I haven't even *had* champagne before, if this is what it tastes like. Maybe it's all been Prosecco in disguise.'

Nate grinned. 'Amazing, right?'

Evie smiled, a little sadly. 'Scarlett would have loved this.' But actually it felt right, that they were somewhere she would have loved.

'Tell me about her.' Nate's voice was barely more than a murmur. But she heard something more – almost a plea. So Evie began to speak. It was impossible to get across the *essence* of Scarlett, but she tried. Nate laughed at all the right moments, leaning towards her as she spoke, his gaze intent on hers, lapping up the information like he *needed* to hear it, almost as much as she found she needed to tell it. She *wanted* to talk about Scarlett, and she was so glad to be remembering her, even if there were parts of it – the stories she told – that made her want to cry. But the tears felt right, and Nate didn't even comment on them, seeming to accept them as part of the memories.

At some point they finished their champagne, and Nate ordered another two glasses. 'I wish I could have known her,' he said, and Evie felt her chest tighten. He met her, didn't he, for a second? She didn't know exactly how it had all played out – and actually she wasn't sure she wanted to. But he would have met her, before she went into the road to get his bike.

'I... I know it sounds stupid, but I feel like I need to know her,' he continued. 'She... well, I'm not sure if she saved my life, because I don't know what would have happened if she hadn't been there – maybe Tasha would have hit the bike instead. Or maybe she would have hit me.'

Evie nodded slowly. 'Maybe you would have got up, kept walking.' *Maybe my best friend wouldn't have died.*

Maybe. That was the thing, wasn't it?

'Yeah.' Nate paused, staring at his champagne, at the bubbles rising to the surface. 'She smiled at me,' he said quietly. 'Before she died. She was a little annoyed, a little impatient, I think.' A flitter of a smile crossed his lips, and Evie felt her own lips copy the action. She could imagine it. Scarlett, annoyed, impatient, wanting to get on with her day. But a kindness there – sometimes hidden, but always there. It was that kindness that would have made her stop, go to help. 'But she smiled at me,' Nate finished. She felt it from him then. The way he was lost in the memory, replaying it. Did he think about it a lot, the accident?

He looked up from his champagne, and she felt the full force of his gaze.

'I don't know if this is the right thing to say, but you were lucky, I think, to have a friend like her.'

Evie sipped her champagne to fight the lump in her throat and avoided looking at him. It didn't *feel* like luck. She almost snapped at him, felt the telltale anger slide into her gut. But she made herself stop, think. Would she change it, if she could? Not the accident, but meeting Scarlett. Would she take it back, so that she didn't have to feel like this now? She remembered it so clearly, the moment they met, Scarlett scowling at her across the A&E room in hospital.

No, she thought firmly. She wouldn't. Because it was worth it – this grief – to have had Scarlett in her life.

'I don't know how to explain it to most people,' she said, twisting the stem of her glass between her fingers. 'A "friend" doesn't really sum it up. People get it if you say a parent or sister or partner. But a "friend", well, I don't know. To so many people, it doesn't seem strong enough. But she was…' She waved a hand in the air, thinking of the right word. 'My person.' She smiled softly. 'Like Meredith and Cristina in *Grey's Anatomy*.'

'Huh?'

'It's just… this thing, that Scarlett and I used to do.'

Nate nodded slowly. 'I don't think I have a friend like that. But I think I get the person-thing. My brother,' he added, when Evie looked at him in question. 'Noah.'

'Your brother?' She realized now how little she knew

about him. She'd known Nate had a brother, but only in the abstract sense.

'Yeah. He's my person, I guess. I think he's a bit bemused by my general lifestyle, but he's the person I'd choose to… you know. Call. Do the Best Man speech. That kind of thing.'

Evie cocked her head. 'Bemused?' It felt like a funny word to use.

Nate's mouth crooked into half a smile. 'He's the traditional type. Married to a smart, successful woman who drinks green tea and smoothies.'

'Sounds awful,' Evie said drily. 'The green tea,' she said quickly, 'not the married part.'

Nate laughed. 'Not a green-tea fan?'

'I tried…' Or, more accurately, *Scarlett* had made her try, because she'd been insisting that Evie give everything a go – anything that might improve her health after her diagnosis. 'But it wasn't for me. I'm a milk-and-sugar girl, I'm afraid. So,' she said, with an attempt at brightness, 'you just have the one sibling then – your brother?'

Nate hesitated for a beat too long, given that it wasn't a difficult question. 'Yeah. Anyway,' he continued, talking slightly more quickly now, 'Noah sort of thinks that the travelling is something I should have *done* by now, given I'm thirty-two. My mum, too – she says she's happy if I'm happy, but there's this implication that I can't *really* be happy doing it.'

'And you are? Happy travelling?'

'I love it,' Nate said. 'I love meeting all the new people, seeing new things. Love the sense that you never know what you might discover, the next time you get on the plane. I love… Okay, this is going to sound bad.'

'All the best things do.' It got a grin out of him.

'I love that no one *expects* anything of me, because I'm always the new person and everyone knows I won't be staying long.'

It would be difficult, though, to make connections that way, wouldn't it, Evie mused. Then again, who was she to talk? She was avoiding connections herself, in a completely different way. She'd pulled away from everyone except Scarlett – and maybe even, if she was being totally honest with herself, from Scarlett a little too. There was no one except Henry depending on her, and she'd made it clear that people should not expect anything of her. Which was worse? Nate's life was so different from hers. His world was still so big, whereas hers had compressed right down. *And whose fault is that, hmm?* She wasn't sure if it was her voice or Scarlett's in her mind.

'I hate being in one place for too long,' Nate carried on, unaware of the thoughts spreading through Evie's mind. 'In fact,' he made a face, 'it might be the longest I've been in one place right now.'

'You're staying with your brother, right?'

'Yeah. Mum's moved to a little one-bed, so she has no room. Camille – Noah's wife Liz – is getting a bit annoyed, I think, but my brother would never kick me out.'

'What about your dad?'

'Well, my parents got divorced.'

'I remember, you said.'

'Right, well, I wasn't sure if you remembered, what with the fear of tumbling to your death and all,' he said with a little smirk.

'It was a legitimate fear! You're just, weirdly, not scared.' She frowned. 'What *are* you scared of?'

He shrugged. 'Don't know. Suppose I'll find out, when I discover it. But no point worrying over what I *might* be scared of. And generally I try not to be scared – because mostly we're scared of things we can't control, and that seems a bit bizarre.'

'Fear of tumbling to death seems pretty controllable to me,' Evie said drily. 'Just don't climb up a massive cliff.'

'Yes, but,' Nate said, a hint of impatience creeping into his voice, 'you're as likely to die from… I don't know, swallowing a hidden piece of glass in a takeaway sandwich.'

Evie raised her eyebrows. 'Is that likely?'

'I think I read about it somewhere.'

It reminded her of her mum. 'So you abstain from takeaway, do you?'

'God, no. I practically live off them while I'm in London. Because that's what I mean – you don't *know* what will happen, so you might as well do all the stuff you can while you can.'

Evie went quiet, the whole thing hitting a little too close to home. Scarlett didn't know, when she got up that morning, that it would be the last time she ever got out of bed. She didn't know, when she stepped off the street to help a stranger, that it would be the final thing she did.

Nate seemed to realize what he'd said, and his face turned sombre as he placed a hand on top of hers on the bar. 'I'm sorry. I shouldn't have… I don't always think things through.'

Evie gave him a wry look. 'I've noticed.' He made a face and she shook her head. 'It's true, I guess. Scarlett was healthy, happy and young. And then she died, in an accident that no one could have predicted.' It was the first time she'd said that out loud in front of him, and she felt his intent gaze on her face as she said the word. *Accident.*

Someone opened the door to the bar and Evie heard it – the soft murmur of live music, filtering in from a different room. She looked for it automatically. 'Where's that coming from?'

Nate cocked his head, as if listening. 'There's dinner and dancing in the main restaurant.' In one quick movement he put down his glass, got to his feet. 'Come on, let's go look.'

He grabbed her hand, practically pulled her down from the bar stool and through the hotel to another room, where they hovered outside. She could see the live band through the glass double doors. Most people were still sitting, rather than up on the small space at the front of the room, but there was an old couple dancing, in a practised way that Evie couldn't help find endearing, and a younger couple, smiling at each other, aglow with new love perhaps.

Nate peered through the doors. 'Shall we dance?'

'I doubt they'll let us in, Evie said, glancing at the doorman. 'Plus, it's not exactly Taylor Swift, is it?'

Nate laughed, but then his face turned contemplative as he watched the band. 'I love music too,' he said, almost like an admission. 'All kinds, Taylor Swift included, but I listen to classical music when I go to sleep. I could never play it – my music skills are much like my painting skills – but I went through a phase as a teenager of not being able to sleep very well.' He shook his head like he was shaking away the memory. 'I kept up the habit and now, when I travel, it's the one thing that stays constant, so I know I can always sleep, no matter where I'm going to wake up.' He smiled at her. 'Let's dance.'

He said something to the doorman, who let them in – how he did it was beyond Evie. She was beginning to suspect that he was a bit of a charmer.

This room was grander than the bar. Less modern, more like something out of an old-fashioned film where ballroom dancing was par for the course. There were white stone pillars at the front where the band was – a violinist among them, Evie clocked. Around the room there were white-clothed tables, candles in the middle of each one, the whole room flickering with their light. On one side there was a massive mirror, with golden rectangles all across it so that it looked like a gigantic French door. The candlelight danced there too.

Nate was pulling her towards the dance floor, but there were still so many people sitting down, so many people who would be watching them and… 'Nate,' she said, biting her lip. He stopped, looked at her. 'I can't dance.'

'That's okay.' He smiled – as usual. 'I can. I'm actually

all right at it, learned for a piece I was writing while I was in Argentina.'

'You're not going to suggest the Argentine tango, are you? Because I'm not really sure that's the right vibe.'

He laughed, tugged on her hand. 'Come on.'

Evie stayed rooted to the spot. 'I'm serious. I'm less Baby in *Dirty Dancing* and more Hugh Grant in *Love Actually*.'

'Well, I'll be all Whatshisname in *Footloose*.'

She laughed and the sound felt almost foreign. 'Again, wrong sort of music.' But she appreciated the effort to join in the game – and couldn't help but think that maybe Scarlett would have appreciated it too.

'Come on.' Nate grabbed her hand again, and she found her fingers lacing with his automatically. He practically dragged her, apparently not noticing that she stumbled more than once, through the restaurant and out onto a terrace.

It was quieter out there, just a few people smoking down one end of the terrace, making Evie realize how loud the hum of conversation inside had been. It was still warm, though a cool breeze brought goosebumps to her bare arms.

'There,' Nate said. 'Now no one can see if we make complete fools of ourselves.'

She pressed her lips together. She was so damn obvious to read, wasn't she? But she thought of what Astrid had said. *You should go out and dance and laugh then.*

Evie could still hear the music from the band. Quieter, but almost more powerful because of it. She heard the violin above the rest of the instruments. The sound slid through her, making her insides thrum.

Her muscles quivered slightly as she looked at Nate, as he put his arms around her. Gently, his touch barely more than a whisper. Her heart hammered at the contact, at the feel of him against her, the subtle smell of aftershave. He took her hand in his, placed the other on her hip, and beneath her dress her skin heated.

'I might fall,' she whispered. 'I tend to do that, sometimes.'

He smiled. 'That's okay.' His eyes were on hers, so close now – close enough to breathe the same air. He spun her in a circle and, even though it was slow, even though she knew she was ungraceful, her breath caught. Her gaze snapped to his the moment she came back to face him, her eyes automatically finding his. On her waist, his thumb moved, a subtle, gentle caress.

'Don't worry,' he murmured as he spun her again. 'I'll catch you, if you fall.'

Chapter Twenty

I watch them dance. Nate was right: he is pretty good at it. He knows exactly how to move Evie so that she doesn't have to try too hard, so that she can rely on him to counteract the natural stiffness in her movements. She'll never be a dancer. That was part of the fun – the fact that we were *both* terrible. But right now, watching her as she twirls and steps into his arms, the music playing softly in the background, moonlight catching Evie's face every time she looks up at him – well, she looks pretty damn graceful.

I feel something bubble inside me. Laughter, I realize. It feels like laughter. Because she was wrong: she *is* exactly like Baby in fucking *Dirty Dancing*.

She has come alive tonight, Evie. I'm so proud of her. And she was right. That teenager was right, even fucking *Nate* was right. I don't want to be mourned. That was never my style. I want people to remember me, obviously. I don't want to be forgotten. But I want people to laugh, about the ridiculous things I did. I want them to feel *happy*, that I lived, that I was a part of things. I would rather be spending my thirtieth birthday – the birthday I'll never have – watching my best friend dance under the stars at the fucking Ritz than I would see her wallow in sadness at home, alone. Even if the man she's dancing with, the man who is looking at her like that, is Nate.

Typical, isn't it? She is doing the things I would have wanted her to do, and she's doing them for *me*, but only because I'm dead.

I think it's only because I'm so in tune with what Evie must be feeling right then that I notice it: the way the violin seems to steal the show, asking questions that none of the other instruments can answer. Nate spins her on exactly the right note – he might not be able to play, but there's no doubt he is musical – and Evie's breath catches as she comes back round to face him. She has forgotten, in that moment, that she said she can't dance. She has forgotten the fear of falling, the fear that her body might give up on her. I don't know how long it will last – maybe only seconds. But for those seconds my friend is lost to the beat, the rhythm of the dance.

And I find that, despite a lot of evidence to the contrary, despite the fact that I *do* still think he's reckless, I trust Nate. I trust him to catch her, if she falls.

The scene shimmers, changing shape in front of me, and I feel myself pulled away from the outskirts and towards the centre. I'm in a bar, dim lighting, but more rustic and sticky-floored than the Ritz by far. It is hot inside, the doors flung open, though there is rain cascading down from the open doorway. Around me, people are chatting and drinking, and everyone keeps glancing expectantly towards the corner of the pub – the corner where Evie is standing, frowning down at a violin.

Ireland. We came here for a couple of weeks, after university and before we moved to London. It rained almost constantly, despite being summer, but we had a great time. We spent a week in Dublin, then a week travelling around, and right now we are in the countryside. We are staying at some hotel down the road, I think, and after going for a walk have stumbled across this pub. It's so delightfully Irish – and until moments ago everyone had been dancing. One of the barmen has finished his shift and is standing next to me, all twinkly eyes and charming smile. Liam? I'm pretty sure his name is Liam.

I tried Irish whiskey that night, and I can feel the effect it's having on my body, how it's making me all warm and brave, and like I want to be up there, dancing.

'Is your friend okay?' Liam asks, with a nod towards Evie. He'll be just a fling, I know now, but I can feel the excitement fizzing through me as he leans towards me – and really is there anything as sexy as an Irish accent?

'Come on,' I say and take his big, warm hand in mine. 'Let's go find out.' I pull him to the corner, where Evie is getting ready to play. I can't remember why, exactly, she's been roped into playing, but she's currently flicking through the music book propped on the stand in front of her, looking anxious.

'You okay, Eves?' I say when we reach her. I drop Liam's hand. No need to be clingy, after all.

She nods, looking at the page, not at me – reading a language I have never been able to understand. Then she bites her lip and glances around the crowd.

189

'You'll be great,' I say. 'And you're way better than that guy.' I jerk my head behind me. To where? The guy who was playing before her, presumably.

'I don't know what to play,' she moans. 'And this violin, it doesn't like me.' She gives it a suspicious look and I laugh, and Evie's lips twitch in a way that reassures me that she was *trying* to make me laugh. She's always doing that – speaking about violins like they are living things with real feelings.

'Play *Pirates*?' I suggest, and Evie makes a face. She won't want to – that's something she only does with close friends, too embarrassed otherwise.

Another guy, slightly older than us, comes up and gives Evie a big smile. 'You ready, *chara*?' Friend – I'm pretty sure I remember that means friend. Maybe he sees the uncertainty in her eyes, because he says kindly, 'You don't have to do it, it's just nice to have some live music, and your friend here says there's no one better.'

I shoot Evie a guilty look at that. So, it was me who volunteered her then. I find I'm not surprised by this.

'It's okay,' she says. 'I'll play a couple. Tell me, though, if it's no good, or you want me to stop or—'

'You'll be grand!' the older man reassures her. 'Whatever you play'll be great craic, I'm sure.'

He leaves us be, and Evie looks down at the music sheet again. 'Suppose I'll have to get used to this, if it's what I want to do for a living,' she mutters.

'Exactly!' I say, and I actually clap my hands in front of me.

She nods and gives the violin a firm look. 'We can do this, you and I.' Then she starts to play. Liam immediately pulls me onto the makeshift dance floor – they'd pushed the chairs to the side earlier that evening to make space. The music starts slow, and Liam's hands are on my back, grazing just under my top. I can feel the way he is watching me and, at the look that passes between us, the fizzing in my stomach starts up again.

This is all happening before Evie's diagnosis, obviously. Before she started getting her first symptoms. And she is glorious, once she gets into the rhythm of it. Once she forgets to be nervous. The music becomes faster, more people get to their feet to join in the dancing and when I glance at Evie I see her smiling, that small, content smile that she gets when she plays. Or that she used to get, I suppose.

The bar is alive now. Drinks shoved to one side, people spinning and laughing. How late is it? I have no idea. Late, presumably, from the blackness outside, the stacks of empty glasses at one end of the bar, the way the candles have burned right down. But with the music there is a fresh wave of energy, and it is Evie making that possible. She is both sidelined – people not looking at her, dancing rather than watching as she plays in the corner of the room – and centre-stage, because this is *all* about her.

'She's good, your friend,' Liam murmurs to me, using it as an excuse to lean in, his breath caressing my ear.

And then the music changes and it is *our* song, mine and Evie's. I laugh, delightedly, and look over at her. She

191

is grinning at me, playing from memory now, a song she knows so well, and I can see she's forgotten that she was self-conscious. I pull away from Liam and dance on my own – ridiculously, because that's the rule – and hear him laugh and clap behind me. Mine and Evie's gaze meet, lock and I feel a wave of love for her. I don't think I told her enough how much I admired her ability to take a piece of music and bring it to life like this. I see other people turn to Evie now, smiling, clapping, shooting each other approving looks.

I doubt she notices, though, because she is playing and I am dancing, and in that moment, that one tiny moment, we are not just the only people in that little Irish bar. We are the only people in the whole fucking world.

Chapter Twenty-One

Next to her on her office desk, Evie's phone buzzed.

> **Hi Evie, I don't mean to pressure you, but did you get a chance to look for Scarlett's designs? Kind regards, Jason.**

Her stomach churned. She hadn't told him that she'd found the dress. She would, she told herself. But for now she put her phone aside and went back to scrolling through listings on SpareRoom. She was trying to find somewhere in London she could move to, where she could still easily commute to the office. Somewhere that was affordable and didn't have five other people living there.

'Evelyn.'

Evie jumped as Henry came up to her desk, quickly minimizing the internet window. Suzy gave Evie a side-eyed look, then immediately focused on her own screen when Henry glanced at her.

'Yes?' Evie asked meekly, wondering if she was about to get told off for using 'office time' for 'personal time', something that was enormously hypocritical, but which Henry liked to bring up as a problem almost monthly at the team meetings where Evie took minutes.

'I need you to stay a bit later today. I've got an evening meeting and we'll need someone to do the coffees.'

'I can't,' Evie blurted out, before she could think better of it. Henry frowned at her. 'I said I'd meet someone,' she babbled, feeling heat blossom under the high-necked top she was wearing. 'And I'm supposed to get on the train, and I need to get to Windsor and…'

'I can do it,' Suzy piped up. 'My husband is getting the kids from school today, so I don't mind staying on a few extra hours if Evie can't.'

Evie shot her a grateful smile.

Henry hesitated. 'Ah, no. That's okay. I'll manage.' He frowned at Evie for a second more – but if it wasn't essential enough that he'd use Suzy, even with her record of going a bit rogue on coffee orders, then it was arguably not essential enough that he could force Evie to do it.

Evie let out a breath as Henry walked away. But she couldn't help the tiniest smile from creeping onto her face. For the first time in a long while she'd decided to have a goddamn backbone.

'Is that true then?' Suzy asked. 'Windsor, is it? I tell you, I'd love to live there. Do you think it gets clogged up with tourists, though, wanting to see the Queen on holiday and all that?'

'Not sure,' Evie said as she pulled her phone towards her. She unlocked it, brought up the message Nate had sent her that morning. **If you're not doing anything this evening, I have a proposition for you. Any chance you can get to Windsor for around 6.30 p.m.?**

Then a follow-up message, before she'd even read the first: **As long as you like horses, that is?**

She'd not replied, mostly because she hadn't decided what to say to him. She *did* like horses, not that she had much experience with them. But Windsor? It seemed like a big deal, getting on a train, travelling all the way there. At the end of the day, no less. But her fatigue hadn't been as bad today – so far – and now she seemed to have made the decision, didn't she? So she replied. **Yes, I can make it. Text me where to meet you?**

'Yes,' Evie said decisively. 'I'm going to Windsor.'

'Oh, that'll be lovely, that will,' Suzy said, beaming. Then she offered Evie the packet of sweets from next to her computer. 'Fizzy cola bottle?'

A riding stables. Where they rode actual horses – that was where he'd asked to meet her. And now Evie was getting a hat shoved on her head by a girl who looked barely older than Astrid, and who was currently asking Evie to wobble her head around to see if it fitted. She'd tried riding once before – she and Scarlett had gone together while they were on holiday in the New Forest. She'd loved it actually, but it wasn't the kind of thing she'd been able to afford, growing up.

The teenager led Evie and Nate to 'meet' their horses. Evie's was a black gelding called Merlin, and when she held her fingers out to touch his nose, he huffed warm breath onto her hand and his eyes watched her, ears pricked forward, like he was trying to figure her out.

Evie noticed that Nate kept giving her furtive glances, and she turned to him while they waited for the horses to be led out the stables and towards the mounting block. 'What?' she asked.

'I just... I thought you might be more... reluctant.' He offered her one of his sheepish smiles and he looked so ridiculous, standing there in walking boots and a black hard hat, with the number fifty-eight written on the back of it, that she couldn't help the smile that pulled at her lips. *Not exactly Rupert Campbell-Black in Jilly Cooper*, she imagined telling Scarlett.

'I wouldn't have come if I didn't like horses, thanks to your warning.' She followed Merlin to the block, as the teenager – really, was she qualified enough to be handling all this? – pulled down the stirrups and tightened the girth. Evie had never really been scared of horses, the way some people were. She knew you could get into accidents on and around them, obviously, but they'd always seemed so gentle to her – and she doubted anyone was going to let someone with her level of experience set off at a wild gallop across Windsor Park.

Evie crossed over to Merlin again, who put his head down, like he was allowing her to reach more of him. His lip twisted in a soppy expression when she scratched him, which made her grin.

Nate was still watching her. '*What?*' she asked again.

He smiled. 'Just trying to figure you out, that's all.'

She rolled her eyes. 'I'm not exactly difficult to figure out.'

'I'm not so sure about that,' he said, in a way that made it difficult to keep looking at him.

The teenager got them both on their horses – Nate's was a brown one (bay, the girl told her) called Diva and, to be fair, she did keep giving Nate diva-ish looks as he got on.

Evie found herself settling into the rhythm of Merlin's walk, the sound of his hooves on the road, and then on grass as they hit a path that took them through trees, the evening summer sunlight glinting between the leaves. Her muscles seemed to relax too, and it was an odd sensation, given that she was used to the opposite. It was an adult woman, thankfully, who was taking them out on the ride, and both Nate and Evie's horses seemed to automatically follow her horse, so that Evie barely had to try and steer.

'So is this for another article?' she asked, having to twist round a little so that she could see Nate behind her – her horse liked going in front apparently.

'No, believe it or not, this was a Christmas present from my nieces, which I haven't used yet.'

'Your nieces?'

'Yeah. They're twins. Natalie and Naomi.'

'Ns, huh?'

Nate rolled his eyes dramatically, the action comical under the hard hat. 'Camille, Noah's wife, insisted that it was a tradition.'

'And it's not?'

'Only if one generation makes a tradition – my parents' names aren't N-names – but Noah told me that it would be tradition, going forward.' Nate's expression turned baffled as his horse put her head down to have a snack on the grass. He just sat there, looking at his reins, until their guide told him what to do, and Evie tried not to laugh. 'Anyway,' Nate continued, once Diva had decided to keep moving, 'they're both very into horses at the moment, so they decided that my Christmas present from the family should be a riding experience, and for some reason Noah went along with it.'

'Well, I think it's a brilliant present,' Evie said decisively, looking around at the park. It really was gorgeous – there was nothing like all this green, late in the evening, during a British summer. She took a deep breath of the warm air, felt like she could taste the freshly mown grass. 'Your nieces clearly have great ideas,' she added. She gave her horse a friendly pat. 'Don't they, Merlin?'

'You should meet them,' Nate called from behind her, so that Evie had to look over her shoulder again.

'Huh?'

'Natalie and Naomi. And Noah. And Camille, I suppose. We have a family dinner every Sunday – and don't tell me, I know that sounds ridiculously perfect of us. But you should come.'

Evie had absolutely no idea how to respond to that. An activity was one thing, but a family dinner quite another. What was this? Were they friends now, as simple as it had been with Astrid? Did she even *want* to be friends with Nate? Underneath her, she felt Merlin tense slightly, his ears flickering back towards her. Maybe she was so in tune with him because she'd had to get used to constantly assessing the tension in her own body.

'Sssh,' she murmured, stroking him again, and he relaxed, ears forward once more. So it was true then – horses really could pick up what you were feeling.

'We'll try a trot here!' called the woman, saving Evie from having to answer Nate. 'Try to stand up and down with the rhythm. One-two, one-two.'

Evie did better than Nate at the trotting, Diva giving him those same suspicious looks, until she clearly decided that he was too terrible and slowed to a walk, resolutely refusing to trot any more.

'Have you done this before?' he asked Evie suspiciously.

'Once.'

'You're doing so well for a beginner,' the woman said with a smile. 'You must have natural rhythm.' She supposed she did, Evie thought. Because fine, she couldn't dance to save her life – *unless*, a sly voice whispered in the back of her mind, *you're in the arms of a certain man* – but she could play, couldn't she? Even if not physically any more, she knew *how* to play. And playing music, well, you had to have rhythm for that, didn't you?

'We'll take the horses into the water up here,' the woman said, turning towards a little lake, surrounded by trees. At this, Evie felt her face change. Sitting on top was one thing, but what: were they supposed to go *swimming*? The woman laughed at her expression. 'The horses like to play in the water, maybe have a drink, that's all.'

It turned out that 'playing' meant 'splashing', and both Merlin and Diva used their front legs to splash the water all around them, spraying both Nate and Evie. Nate was holding onto the front of the saddle rather gingerly as his horse splashed, and suddenly the whole thing felt ridiculously funny, and Evie burst out laughing. Proper laughter, the kind that rises inside you and leaves you light, and unable to stop smiling.

Happy. In that moment, sitting on a horse, splashing in the lake, and looking at Nate's very suspicious expression, she felt honestly *happy*. And maybe that was okay. Because Scarlett would have wanted her to grab hold of it, this fleeting moment of happiness, wouldn't she? Even if it was with Nate?

Nate chuckled too, shaking his head slightly, then turned to smile at her. Evie stopped laughing, but the lightness in her lingered for a beat longer. His gaze met hers, so warm and kind, and even though she could list endless reasons why it was a bad idea, even though she knew she should not be feeling like this, Evie's heart stuttered.

Chapter Twenty-Two

She'd had to get a bus on the way there, so on the way back Nate drove her to the nearest train station – Windsor & Eton. He'd offered to drive her all the way back to Clapham, but she'd refused. Partly because that long in a car together would feel intense, and partly because it would probably be quicker anyway to get the train. And at this time in the evening she'd get a seat – which she needed. Riding had not been as tiring as she had expected, though, and she'd asked the woman who'd taken them out for the price list, after Nate had insisted that his birthday voucher covered her ride too. It wasn't something she could afford to do on a regular basis, for sure, but maybe something to think about.

Nate got out of the car and walked her to the entrance of the station. Even the train station here was posh – it looked more like a town house, and there was a brick archway you walked under to get to the platform. Evie stopped to face Nate just before the archway.

'Thank you for inviting me.'

He nodded, shoved his hands in his pockets. His usual messy hair was somewhat flattened by the hat he'd been wearing. 'Wasn't sure you'd come.'

'No. I wasn't sure, either,' she admitted. 'But I'm glad I did. That was...' She smiled. 'Pretty cool.'

He hesitated. 'I, er, looked it up.' Rusty, she'd once thought his voice was. But it wasn't really. It was deep and had a slightly husky edge to it, but it was also somehow soothing – the kind of voice you'd want to listen to on an audiobook.

'Looked *what* up?'

'Horse-riding and MS.'

Evie went alert, the way she always did when her illness was brought up. It was silly. She should be used to talking about it by now. Or at the very least she should *get* used to it, given it wasn't going anywhere. But she'd never liked the idea of people 'researching' her condition, once they found out about it. 'Oh?' she said, trying to make her voice casual.

'I didn't…' He brought up a hand to rub the back of his neck. 'I don't mean in a weird way. I just wanted to check that it would be okay. Because, well, I didn't want to, you know, force you up a cliff again.' He gave her that sheepish smile – the one that was starting to make *her* smile when she saw it.

'And, what: horse-riding passed the test, did it?' She couldn't work out how she felt about Nate checking. Because yes, she'd flipped out a bit when he'd taken her climbing, but only a *little* bit, really. And there was a part of her that liked the fact that he didn't treat her as broken, that he suggested they did things other people would assume weren't possible for her. But then there *were* some things she couldn't do. She couldn't live as she had before, and it would be stupid to ignore that.

'Yeah, well, apparently it can be helpful, actually. For balance and mobility. In case you wanted to know,' he added, with a little awkward shrug.

She looked at him, standing there looking all flustered and awkward – but only because he'd thought of her. Because he'd thought to check, had thought to care.

'Thank you,' she said softly, and his gaze found hers. And then, without thinking too hard about it, Evie stepped towards him and kissed him lightly on the cheek. He stiffened. She *swore* he stiffened, his hands clenched into fists by his sides, like he didn't want her near him – not like that – and didn't want to say, to offend her. Not that she meant it like that, she only meant it in a friendly way, Jesus, and she—

She backed away, feeling heat rise in her chest. But he stopped her, his hands wrapping around her arms, holding her in place. Her breath caught.

And then he was kissing her, actually kissing her, his mouth hot and demanding on hers, and without even thinking about it, Evie hooked her arms around his neck, pulling him to her because, Jesus, the very touch of him had her core pulsing, her skin sparking in a way she'd never—

No. The word was in her mind first, then out loud, and she pushed away from him, bringing a hand to her mouth. She shook her head frantically. 'No,' she repeated. What had she been *thinking*?

'Okay,' Nate said, his breathing a little heavy. He pulled a hand through his flattened hair. 'Okay, sorry.'

'I can't do this,' she said, her voice high-pitched, panicked.

His eyes stayed level with hers as he took a step towards her.

'No!' she said again. 'I can't do it.' She felt a sob building in her even as she squashed it down.

He nodded, but he was still looking at her in that intense way, a way that made her skin burn. She really thought, though, that he'd leave it at that.

Then, 'Why?' he asked. Not demanding, and he didn't move towards her again, but rather shoved his hands in his pockets, as if making his intention not to touch her very clear. But still, the question. Why?

'Why?' she repeated incredulously. '*Why?* Nate, I can't even get into that – the answer should be obvious.' She shook her head, pulled both hands through her hair. It was knotted, she noticed, probably from the damn hat. She didn't want to state it out loud, didn't want to throw it at him, not after he'd been so kind to her. But, Jesus, he was the reason Scarlett was dead; she couldn't *forget* that, couldn't start *kissing* him, for Christ's sake.

But regardless of the fact that she tried to keep it bottled in, he clearly read something in her eyes. 'I thought you said it was an accident,' he said, ever so quietly. And she saw it, the flash of hurt in his eyes.

She closed her own eyes. 'It was,' she whispered. 'But I can't just…' She opened her eyes to see him still standing there, watching her. Waiting. And she felt it bubble over – yet again around him. 'You don't get it!' she snapped. 'It's okay for you, isn't it? You're constantly moving around, making new friends. And you've got your brother and you live your life in this… *careless* way, like nothing bad has ever happened to you, so how . . . *how* could you possibly know how I feel right now?'

She was breathing too heavily and he was nodding, letting her spit at him. 'I get that,' he said evenly.

She crossed her arms, not wanting to look directly at him for too long. 'You get it, do you?' She tried, and failed, to stop the bitterness creeping into her voice.

'Yeah.' And then a spark of anger lit his face, and she saw the muscles in his arms tense. 'Look, Evie, I might be reckless and careless, and I will regret every fucking day of my entire fucking life what happened that day with Scarlett. I still hear it.' He took his hands out his pockets, shook out his fists like he was shaking something off. 'I still hear the sound of…' He shook his head, stopped himself. 'So I get it. Truly. But you are not the only person to have lived through stuff, okay? I know you're having a shit time of it – I know who Scarlett was to you; and I know you've got this thing, this illness, that I can't understand, but it's not like my life has been free from any kind of grief.'

There was a pause and when he spoke again, Evie's heart spasmed. 'My brother killed himself,' he said flatly.

She stared at him, throat growing dry. 'What? Noah, he—'

'No.' Nate let out a breath. 'No, not Noah. We had another brother. Nick. The middle one, between me and Noah. When I was fifteen and he was twenty-one, he killed himself. He'd had it rough, ended up in prison for six months for something stupid – stealing something –

and when he came out, he couldn't find a job and…' He heaved another breath. 'Not the point. I don't even know the full story, anyway. I got more than my parents thought I did, at fifteen, but not the whole story.'

She tried to think of something to say. Couldn't.

Been to many funerals, have you?

One.

One. His brother's. His *brother* had died. Killed himself. When Nate was just a teenager.

She thought of something else too. He listened to music, every night, to go to sleep. Every night, since he was a teenager. Since this had happened and had ripped something from him, so that he couldn't sleep without it.

'Oh my God,' Evie whispered, and brought her hand to her mouth before lowering it slowly. 'Nate. I am so, so sorry.' It was her turn, this time, to step towards him. And his turn to back away from her.

'Yeah, well.' There was silence, and neither of them could look at each other. Then she heard the station tannoy announcing the arrival of her train in one minute. He nodded towards the archway behind her. 'You better go.'

She bit her lip. But what was she supposed to do? What was she supposed to say? 'Okay,' she said quietly. But she turned back to look at him before she went through the archway. 'I'm sorry, Nate,' she said again.

He met her gaze then, finally. 'Yeah. Me too.'

Chapter Twenty-Three

His brother killed himself. When Nate was just fifteen.

I don't even know how to process that. Don't know how to fit it in with the image I've formed of him. I think of him, at my funeral, and I think of the way he spoke to me, in the ambulance. The way he held my hand the whole way.

He always seems so *level*, though. I can't equate it with that kind of loss – not just losing someone, but having them voluntarily leave you. But then maybe I don't know enough. I haven't seen it all the way through, that kind of grief. Haven't seen how you grow and change as a result of it. Without meaning to, I think of my parents and the fact they could never have another child. The fact that now they have lost me. What will that do to them, in the long run?

Then I find myself wondering what Nate was like as a teenager. Whether he was still reckless, in those little ways, whether he always spoke without thinking or whether that came after his brother's suicide.

Nick. He'd said his brother's name was Nick. And now I'm wondering about Nick himself. When he died, did he go through what I went through? Did he relive his memories, forced to be an observer, wanting to change the past, but unable to? Was he around somewhere, in this space I now inhabit? When did it stop? What happened next?

Because it is too much to think about, I turn from those thoughts as best I can. I think of the way Nate kissed Evie, the way he went from so still to so passionate, in the space of a breath. Like there was a moment when he could have decided not to act, and he went for it anyway. I can appreciate that – that need to act.

But *Evie*, I wasn't expecting her to react like that. Whenever I've seen her in relationships before, it always seemed like she was just going along with it, playing a role. She said I didn't get the Will-thing and she's right, I didn't. Not only because I didn't like him, but because she never seemed like her best self when she was with him. She didn't seem like she was passionate about him, and I know she *can* be passionate, because I've seen it, when she plays the violin. I'm pretty sure, though, that the passionate Evie, the one I love, came out to play tonight. Just for a moment – until she remembered.

I don't think we find that kind of passion with another person very often. Maybe we get an echo of it, on nights when we are drunk and excited and everything feels new and shiny and bright. But more than that? My mum used to laugh at me when I said that when I fell in love I wanted it to be *blind*, and *passionate*, and *all-encompassing*. She said that was the kind of filmic love that only got you into trouble. And when I'd asked about her and Dad, she'd said they had a 'different kind of love'. *The steady love is the best love, Scarlett. It's the kind of love that will stick.*

I'd thought I'd had that with Jason. I'd thought I'd had both the passion *and* the possibility for it to turn into something steady.

I'm lying on his bed in the flat in Soho, having had sex with him for the first time. The flat is small, but it's *Soho*, right in the centre of everything, near enough to walk to both my office and the gay bar that everyone at work has taken to going to recently. The flat is well decorated, but then I'd expect nothing less from a man like Jason. He is sophisticated, the way men of my age just aren't yet. There are photographs all around the place – obviously – and a photo of an older woman, staring straight into the camera, is in pride of place above the bed. I'd asked him what was so special about it when he'd brought me back after dinner that evening, trying to cover up my nerves with bravado.

'Because there's such a sense of vulnerability about it, don't you think?' Jason had said. And then he'd distracted me by kissing my neck, peeling my top away from my skin, his hands caressing, soft, confident strokes.

Now, lying naked on top of the duvet, I glance up at the photo and huff. 'It feels like she's watching us.' Jason's fingers tiptoe down my bare arm. He is so goddamn attractive, his body practically a piece of art itself. 'Would you take it down, if I asked you to?' I prompt.

He nuzzles into my neck, his breath warm against my skin. 'If it was a choice between you and her, then yes, definitely.'

I roll onto my side to look at him and I see his gaze sweep the length of my body – no hiding the admiration there. I hesitate, but then I've already decided that I have to ask. If I went home with him tonight, and if it went well, then I'd told myself I had to ask. 'I hear you're married,' I say, keeping my voice even.

He raises his eyebrows. 'Do you now? Talking about me, are you?'

'*Are* you?' I say, refusing to let him play that game.

His fingers stop their dance along my arm. 'I'm separated,' he says eventually.

'There's photos of you together online.' No point in hiding that I've looked – everyone in the office has looked. It's just the way our world works.

He runs a hand down to my waist, leaving pinpricks of warmth behind. 'Yes. Sometimes we still go to events together, you know, to keep up appearances.'

I nod, digesting. I knew, of course. I knew that he was lying – I'd known from the moment I'd met him, if I was being totally honest with myself. But at that point it still felt new and fragile and *vital* – vital enough that we both pretended, for a while.

In the morning we have sex again and when I leave the flat, when he kisses me goodbye, I feel it.

The moment.

I'm sure, right then, that Jason is The One. That, no matter what, this will work out. I'm not so sure now, looking back, but I remember the absolute certainty of it at the time.

When I get back to my flat – which feels ugly in comparison to Jason's – Evie is sitting in the middle of the kitchen. On the floor. Crying. She looks up at me out of red eyes as I rush over to her, dropping my keys in the middle of the floor.

'Will broke up with me,' she sobs.

I put my arms around her. 'Oh, Eves. I'm so sorry.' How long has she been sitting there, refusing to get up? If I'd left Jason's sooner, would I have got back in time to be there with her, before she fell apart like this? 'He's not worth it,' I say firmly and she nods, though I can feel her sagging against me.

'He was cheating on me,' she says and I clench my teeth.

'He is a bastard.' But then, look at what I'm doing with Jason. I was still telling myself that he was *separated*, telling myself to believe him. But would there be another woman crying on the floor like Evie, if she found out that Jason had been with me overnight?

'Come on,' I say and I pull Evie to her feet, take her to the sofa.

'He made it sound like it was because...' She gulps. 'Because the MS, it's changed me.'

'Don't listen,' I say automatically, my words a snap. 'Don't listen, Eves, okay? He's a dick. He's a dick, and it is nothing to do with *you*, it is all on him.' I can see she doesn't believe me. She'd already decided, hadn't she, that her illness had changed her? And maybe I should have got that more. Because maybe the thing is, it *did* change her, but that didn't necessarily mean she wouldn't come out stronger. It didn't make her *less* than she was before – it might just mean there were some things that would be different. I don't think I ever figured out that line: between not letting her MS define her, and allowing for the fact that some things would have to change. I wanted her to be *her*, as she had been before, because I thought that would be the best thing for Evie. And I was so determined to stick to that – that really – that *I* was the one letting it define her in some ways, with my all-or-nothing attitude. I wish I had the chance to say that to Evie in person now, to apologize, to help her figure out that balance.

But then again, maybe I'm not the only one who will be able to do that.

Chapter Twenty-Four

Evie knocked hesitantly on Astrid's door, clutching a bottle of white wine. Not the cheap stuff she had stored in the fridge – she'd actually gone out to the shop and brought some Chablis. And given that it was wine she was holding, maybe she should be thinking of it as Julie's house, not Astrid's. But it was Astrid who opened the door, smiled at her. She'd taken to putting some kind of product in her now-short hair, so that it stuck up all punk-like.

'The black's growing out,' Evie said by way of greeting.

'Yeah. We'll need to re-dye it. Come on,' she said, gesturing Evie inside. 'Mum's in the kitchen.'

Evie was pretty sure Astrid must have told her mum about Scarlett, because she'd got an invitation to dinner not long after that. Not wanting to be rude, and because Astrid was growing on her, she'd said yes, and now here she was, Friday night, clutching a bottle of wine and being ushered into the small kitchen, where she could smell frying onions.

Their kitchen was much nicer than Evie and Scarlett's. Or hers, she supposed now. It was about the same size, obviously, and the same layout, but there were nice bar stools on one side of the kitchen counter, a fruit bowl with actual fruit in it and a painting of London's skyline up on one wall. The walls were pale blue in the kitchen, something that extended into the adjoining living room, but the place felt warm, despite the colour. There was a throw and fancy cushions over the sofa in the living room, along with a squidgy armchair. Julie had only been here a month or so, and already the place looked more like home than Evie and Scarlett's flat. Evie supposed they'd never really bothered, assuming it would be temporary, and things were even more bare now that she had taken down Scarlett's things.

'Evie!' Julie exclaimed, looking over at her from where she was stirring a pan on the hob. 'I'm so sorry, I'm running a bit behind.' She was wearing a pencil skirt and blouse, her feet bare on the kitchen floor. Still in work clothes, Evie supposed. Her hair was pulled up into a messy bun on the top of her head, and despite her very put-together outfit, there was a sheen of sweat on her brow. 'I'm making risotto – is that okay? I just thought most people like risotto? And are you vegetarian? I forgot to ask. But I've done asparagus risotto, so it's safe, either way.'

She was more flustered than Evie remembered her the last two times she'd caught glimpses of Julie. 'I'm not vegetarian, but I love asparagus *and* risotto.' And she couldn't remember the last time someone cooked for her, she realized. 'I brought wine,' she added, holding up the Chablis.

'Oh, that's so sweet. Thank you. Anna – get the glasses out, will you?'

Astrid did exactly that, and Evie poured her and Julie a glass. She frowned at Astrid. 'You're too young, right?'

Astrid flapped a hand as she got a Coke from the fridge. 'I don't like it anyway.' To which Julie made a small 'hmm' sound from the cooker, now adding some of the wine to the risotto.

Because no one had suggested that she sit anywhere else, Evie perched on one of the bar stools by the kitchen counter, and Astrid pulled up a stool next to her. 'So,' she said. 'I've decided to do this concert.'

'Really? That's great.'

'Isn't it?' Julie said, smiling over at them. 'She's so talented.'

'Mu-u-u-m!' Astrid moaned, though Evie could see her fighting off a smile. She couldn't remember her own mother ever praising her like that. But then she remembered the flowers that Ruth had sent Scarlett's parents, and a worm of guilt wriggled in her stomach.

'Anyway,' Astrid continued, 'I was thinking you could help me.'

'Help you?'

'Yeah. Because if I'm doing it, I want to be good – and, well, they've said that I can have a solo.'

'So clearly you *are* good,' Evie pointed out, taking a sip of her wine.

'Yes, but – it would be useful to have someone to practise with and maybe we could even, like, come up with something ourselves?'

'Compose?' Evie's eyebrows shot up. 'That's not something you can just...' she trailed off, looking for the right words, 'have a bash at.'

'Why?'

'Well… I don't know,' Evie said with a frown. 'Because it's difficult, and takes time to learn.' And that sounded stupid and defeatist.

'Please? We can try, at least. You said you liked being a part of something, remember? When you were in the orchestra or whatever? Well, you'd be a *part* of something, doing this.'

Astrid made the last bit overdramatic, throwing her arms in the air, slightly prodding fun at both herself and Evie. But Evie realized she hadn't been giving the girl enough credit. She'd assumed that because she was a teenager she would be too wrapped up in her own drama to notice certain slips, but she clearly paid attention to *everything*.

'And Mum's no help at all,' Astrid continued, but she said it with a grin at her mother.

'I'm not,' Julie agreed, stirring the risotto. 'So you're musical then, Evie?'

'I—'

'Evie plays the violin.'

Evie huffed out a breath. 'You don't even know if I'm any good.'

'You must be, you have that epic violin. And, well, I *may* have googled you.' Astrid looked down, inspecting her Coke can.

'*May* have?'

'Yeah, there are some videos of you playing on YouTube.'

'There are?'

'Yeah, you've never looked?' She grabbed a phone from the other side of the kitchen counter. 'Here, I'll show you.'

'No,' Evie said quickly. 'No, I don't want to see.'

'Anna,' Julie said with a frown, 'you shouldn't look people up online without their permission – it's a bit… creepy.'

'Astrid,' Astrid corrected.

Julie gave her a side-eyed look as she added stock to the pan. 'That's not your name.'

Astrid stuck her chin in the air. 'Not until I change it.'

'Why don't you like Anna?'

'It's too… soft.'

Julie said nothing to this for a moment, contemplating her daughter, and Evie swore she could see a touch of sadness coming in to claim her face. Then she turned to Evie. 'Sorry,' she said.

'No, don't worry,' Evie replied, not entirely sure whether she was apologizing for the little argument or the fact that her daughter had been cyber-stalking her. She took a sip of wine, studied Astrid over the rim of her glass as Julie went back to cooking. 'How did you even find me? You don't know my surname.'

'Sure I do,' Astrid said easily. 'Jenkins.' Evie tried to remember if she'd ever told her that, but Astrid answered the question for her. 'It's on one of the letters to you, I saw it in your flat.'

Next to the letter to Scarlett, which still sat unopened.

'Practising your private detective skills, are you?' Evie said, with a slightly resigned sigh.

Julie looked over at them, a small smile playing around her lips. Evie had a moment when she wasn't sure what category she fell into: adult friend or teenage daughter?

'So… to conclude,' Julie said, waving the wooden spoon in the air, 'you do play the violin too? That's so nice – we've never met anyone who does it, really.'

'I used to,' Evie said, giving in. 'I had to give it up when I got MS.' She flexed her hand automatically.

'Oh, I'm sorry. My mother has MS.'

'Right, Ast… um…' She looked between mother and daughter, cleared her throat and trailed to a stop.

'My mother had to give up her job too, in the end,' Julie said, rescuing Evie. 'But she was near retirement age anyway and she's an admin assistant, so I think she's rather glad about it, all things considered.' Evie knew Julie didn't mean it badly, that she was only saying it to be kind, but she wasn't sure you *could* be glad about something like that. Being forced to give something up for an illness would always feel like a defeat to her, rather than a victory.

Julie gave her a look, like she knew what she was thinking, and added quietly, 'It's a horrible illness. I don't know what she was like, without it – Mum had it before she had me, so we used to joke that MS was part of the family.' She shook her head. 'I know it's not easy – and I know everyone's MS is different – but if it helps at all, my mother's happy and content, and doing what she wants to do. She and my dad are retired together, and they've both got into their gardening. She gets to boss him around with what goes where, when she gets too tired.'

She smiled at Evie, and Evie found she liked the image: the hope there. Found herself thinking that maybe she'd find someone to sit in the garden with, one day. She could get into gardening, she reckoned – if she had a garden.

'Grandad's going to come here and do an indoor garden for us, isn't he?' She directed the question at Astrid, who rolled her eyes in that brilliantly teenage way. An eye-roll just didn't have the same effect, did it, once you hit twenty?

'Right, sure, an indoor garden – you make that sound so-o-o-o much cooler than it will be.'

Julie served the risotto and, with the three of them chatting, Evie found herself enjoying the company more than she'd thought she would. She had a moment of wishing Julie had moved in earlier – she could imagine herself and Scarlett and Julie all sitting up, drinking wine until too late. Until she realized that, in all likelihood, she'd have resisted spending time with another person, knowing at the end of the day that she'd always have Scarlett to fall back on.

Astrid walked her to the door at the end of the evening. 'So, where did we land on the whole you-helping-me thing?'

'I'll think about it,' Evie hedged.

'Great! I'll come round to practise this weekend then – we'll have to use your place, obviously. Mum says that she gets a headache if I play too much in the house.'

'Only when you get the notes wrong, love,' Julie called from the kitchen. 'I love your playing once you've figured it all out, you know that.'

'Right,' Astrid agreed. 'So, this weekend? When works?'

Evie couldn't help smiling at the way Astrid was manoeuvring her. It reminded her a little of Scarlett, that relentless energy. But this weekend… Nate had invited her round for a family dinner. A dinner she'd never agreed to, but still. Did he even want her to come now? They hadn't spoken since he'd told her about his brother.

'Tomorrow morning, I suppose,' Evie said eventually, because Astrid was still looking at her expectantly.

'Wicked. See you then!'

Maybe it was the two glasses of wine that made her text Nate as she crossed the hallway back to her own flat. **Am I still coming round for dinner on Sunday?**

She got a reply back immediately. **Do you want to?**

She gave herself the time it took to unlock the door and step inside to think about it. She hated the way they'd left things. She didn't know when he'd be off again, jet-setting around the world, and she found that it didn't sit right, the idea that he might leave the country and they'd never see each other again. It didn't sit right that their last conversation might be the final one they'd ever have.

Yes, she typed back.

> Okay, great. It's actually my brother's fortieth this weekend – I forgot when I was talking to you. So come tomorrow night instead? For the party, I mean. We'll all be too hungover for family dinner on Sunday.

I can't gatecrash your brother's birthday! I can come another time.

Too late. I've told Camille you're coming now and she's working out the food and drink. She'll be annoyed if I change it back.

It wouldn't be true, of course, because he'd literally only just confirmed, but she got the point he was making. Another message came through, before she could reply. Texting her the address and then: **See you here at 7. x**

She shouldn't read into the kiss. She was not a bloody teenager. But still, she couldn't help rereading the message exchange before she went to sleep.

Chapter Twenty-Five

Evie has been at the party all of five minutes, and I can tell she's already overwhelmed. She's doing that thing where she hunches over to make herself all small and insignificant – so different from the Evie who played the violin in that pub in Ireland.

They are all in the garden, outside the kind of house I imagined myself living in one day. Three floors, gorgeous Victorian town house, glass sliding doors, a perfect patio, grass that is maybe a little too neatly mown for my liking, but full of summer colour. There are plates of mini-quiches on the patio table, along with a makeshift bar and a barbecue in the corner. Kids are running around and screaming, taking it in turns to dash through a sprinkler.

'Evie!'

Nate's brother – like Nate, with messy dark hair, kind, brown eyes and an air of confidence in his stride – steps towards her, clasping her hand, looking totally delighted that she's there. Nate had called his brother over, introduced Evie and then promptly disappeared, and now Evie is standing there looking mildly panicked.

'Happy birthday!' Evie says, her voice a little squeaky. She thrusts into Noah's hands a bottle of champagne that she bought from the local Sainsbury's on the way there.

'Oh, you're so kind,' Noah says. And he slings his arm around honestly the most beautiful woman I've ever seen in my entire life. Brilliant cheekbones, perfect eyebrows, long blonde hair falling in soft curls all the way to her waist. 'Isn't she kind, Camille?'

'Very kind,' Camille says, as Noah thrusts the champagne into her hands. She gives him a little pat on the arm, while still looking at Evie. 'Thank you for coming. Can I get you a drink? I've made gin cocktails, I'll get you one.' She gives Noah's arm a squeeze. She's wearing white capri pants and open-toed sandals, and I see Noah turn to watch as she walks away. From the way his eyes become soft, I'd guess he's already had a few – but then why the fuck not? I'm realizing now how lucky anyone is to make forty, so if you want to get smashed, get fucking smashed.

'So, Evie,' Noah says. 'Nate says you work in advertising – is that right?'

'Ah…' She clearly doesn't want to have this conversation, and I know why. She doesn't want to admit to this clearly successful man with his white picket-fence lifestyle that she is an assistant in a job that she doesn't have any interest in.

'I quite like that car advert at the moment,' Noah continues. 'What's it called?' Without giving her a chance to answer, he swivels his head towards the open back door. 'Camille! What's that car with the good advert at the moment? The one the girls like?'

'Honda!' Camille calls back, and Noah nods, facing Evie again.

'Honda,' he repeats. 'Was that you?'

Evie is saved from continuing this conversation by Nate, who comes up next to Noah and claps him on the shoulder. 'Noah keeping you entertained, Evie?'

'I was telling her all the horrible stories about you,' Noah says, without missing a beat. They look remarkably similar, standing next to each other. I wonder if Nate will look like this in ten years' time – if so, he'll be lucking out. Will I still be here, watching, in ten years' time? A wave of loneliness washes through me at the thought – the idea that I might always be confined only to watch, never participate. *I*, who was always so sure people were watching me.

'Not possible,' Nate says with a shake of his head. 'There are no bad stories about me, only good.'

'Hmm,' Evie pipes up, and there is a slight glint in her eye – one that has been dulled over the last few years, but one I recognize. 'I'm not sure I'd call what happened on the eleventh of February 2015 "good".' She cocks her head. 'Would you?'

I see the way Nate's gaze flickers to Noah, the wary look that creeps into his eyes as his brow furrows. As he wonders whether there is something he did, something he should be remembering.

Noah, to his credit, immediately plays along. 'I still have nightmares about that day,' he says, putting a hand to his heart dramatically.

Nate flicks his gaze between them, and Evie laughs – that loud, unrestrained laugh that is so contagious when she gives in to it. Noah chuckles too, and Nate punches Noah lightly on the arm. 'Jerk.'

'Well, you shouldn't be so gullible then, should you?'

Noah gets pulled away by a group of his friends, and Nate turns to Evie. 'I was going to say sorry for leaving you, but it seems like you're holding your own.' He thrusts a drink, with a stirrer and raspberries and everything, into her hand. 'Camille said this was for you.'

Evie takes the drink, gulps rather than sips, the action betraying the nerves that must be straining under the surface. I wonder if she notices, though, the way she relaxes when Nate is next to her, the way she angles her body towards him. I wonder if Nate even realizes the way he runs his hand down Evie's back, reassuring, needing to touch. This even after their argument, which neither of them has spoken about.

'Come on, let's sit.' Nate starts manoeuvring her towards one of the patio chairs, when one of Noah's twin girls comes up.

'Will you be the monster?' she asks, blinking her eyelashes at him. We learn to do that early, don't we, us girls?

Nate looks down at her. 'Which one are you again?'

'Natte-e-e-e-e.'

'Right, right. Naomi.'

The girl folds her arms crossly, and Nate slaps his forehead. 'Sorry, Natalie!' I can tell he's only teasing her, that he knows exactly which twin is which. Not that I've any idea how – they look exactly the same to me.

'I'm talking to Evie right now,' Nate says, which earns Evie a suspicious look. 'Maybe later.'

Natalie shakes her head. 'Now!'

'Later.'

'Now.'

'Do you get how negotiation works?'

'Negotiation is usually done on a man's terms,' Evie pipes up, her voice dry. Nate raises his eyebrows, and Natalie blinks at her. 'It means he thinks he can get what he wants because he's a man,' Evie tells her. Then she leans towards her. 'It means you can't give in to it,' she stage-whispers, and Natalie returns her smile in solidarity.

Nate gives Evie that look – the one I've noticed him giving her a few times recently, when he is surprised by her. Then, without warning, he launches towards Natalie, roaring. She screams delightedly and runs away, and Nate, grinning, gestures Evie towards the patio chairs. Posh iron chairs, not cheap plastic ones. 'Let's sit before I get roped in.'

'How do you tell them apart?' Evie asks as she sits down.

'Ah, well, Natalie's always wearing a high ponytail, Naomi favours plaits.'

'And if they don't have their signature hairstyles?'

'Then I don't stand a chance. I'm not even sure *Noah* stands a chance.' It's clearly a joke, though he gives Evie a sly look. 'Like Lindsay Lohan in *The Parent Trap*.'

I feel a rush of jealousy. That's *our* game, mine and Evie's. But it makes Evie laugh, her eyes light up and my jealousy fades. Actually I'm glad she's still playing it. And she'll remember me, won't she? Every time she plays it, she'll remember me.

'Mum!' Nate calls to someone as she comes out the back door – a woman in her late sixties maybe, going grey but owning it, wearing bright-red lipstick and a denim jumpsuit.

'You must be Evie,' she says, smiling at her. Clearly Nate has been talking about Evie, hasn't he? 'I'm Grace,' the woman continues. 'Mother to these two heathens.' She gestures at Nate, leaving Noah implied.

'Nate!' Noah calls from across the patio, gesturing at the barbecue.

Nate sighs. 'Duty calls. Though why they're making me do it is beyond me. Camille would be better at it.'

Grace flaps a hand at him. 'You are a man. Go do manly things. Besides, Camille has done this entire party, so the least you could do is go and prod a few hamburgers.'

'Hey, I planned my whole London trip around this, don't I get credit for that?'

'You want credit just for showing up now, do you? I'll remember that, on *your* fortieth birthday.'

Evie is watching the exchange, and a hint of sadness has crept into her eyes. There are so many things she could be thinking right now: the reminder of birthdays that I won't be there for; the fact that she doesn't have this, the easy relationship with her mother, or any sense of family at all really. I feel that familiar frustration that I can only guess, never know, what the people I've left behind are thinking. I can no longer ask them, and I wonder now if perhaps I should have asked more about how they felt, when I had the chance. Whatever direction her thoughts have gone in, though, Evie hides it, smiles at Grace when Nate leaves. I don't think she notices the pointed look he gives his mother as he heads across the patio – a warning to look after Evie – but I do.

'Nate tells me you went horse-riding?' Grace says when it's just the two of them. Evie flushes, not because of the horse-riding presumably, but because of what happened after. 'I bet he was terrible, was he?'

Evie's lips twitch. 'He was.'

'He thinks he'll be so good at all that stuff – anything sporty, you know – but he never was. He gives everything a go, but he was never destined to be a great athlete.' Without missing a beat, Grace takes Evie's hands in hers. 'I'm sorry, about your friend.'

Well, no point dancing around it, I suppose – it's the only reason Evie is here, after all.

'Thank you,' Evie says. She's getting better at it, I notice, accepting the apology that people give. You'd think that over the years we would have come up with something better than 'I'm sorry for your loss', but no one seems to have thought of anything.

Grace considers Evie. 'It won't go away, that hurt you feel,' she says, matter-of-factly. 'It is stupid for anyone to tell you that time will heal all the wounds or that you'll move on from it. You won't. Not completely.' I know she's thinking about her son, Nick. 'But you *will* learn to live with it.' She squeezes Evie's hands, before dropping them. 'It will be a part of you always, and you will come out the other side of this changed, and that's okay. But it's possible to learn how to keep a space for her in your heart and not let it crush you. I promise you, you can learn that.'

Evie is blinking to stem the tears now, and she drops her gaze from Grace's as she takes a sip of her gin.

'I'm sorry,' Grace says. 'I don't mean to make you sad.'

Evie shakes her head. 'I don't know what's worse at the moment. Talking about it or trying to... I don't know. Get on with things.'

'I know that feeling,' Grace says gently.

Evie nods, though she doesn't reference Nick – I doubt she wants to be the one to bring him up directly. Her shoulders move with the next breath she takes. 'Of the two of us, Scarlett was the brighter one. She made *me* brighter, just by being my friend.'

I don't know how I feel about that. In some ways, I suppose, friends *should* make each other brighter, but she's saying it like only one of us had the space to shine, and she had given that role to me. I think back now to the way she was horse-riding with Nate, the confidence there, and the way he pushed her to climb when I would have let her sit and watch, and can't help wondering if perhaps, instead, I had *claimed* it.

'Well, then,' Grace says, 'you'll take her brightness and keep some of it in you, won't you?'

'Is that what you do? Find a way to keep him still there, still bright, without...'

Without what, Eves? Without regretting it? Resenting it? Without letting it overwhelm you? It is so fucking annoying

229

when she doesn't finish the sentence. So frustrating that I can't demand she tells me what she is thinking.

Grace presses her lips together, looking over at her sons across the patio, and I know she is thinking of how to answer – that she doesn't want to say something for the sake of it. 'I have moments,' she says slowly, 'when it is overwhelming, and I feel so angry that Nick could have left like that, so angry that I didn't do anything to stop it.' Evie sits still, quiet, and I see the way her fingers have tightened on her gin glass. 'But I've tried to accept that *no one* can change what happened, and I've tried to come to terms with the fact that we are all a product of the choices we make. So because there is no way to change anything, I do my best to be grateful for what I did have, and I try to keep the good parts of him alive with me. To remember more than the end.'

She smiles at Evie, though I see the effort it takes to do so.

'We had a dog when the boys were little, and Nick, he was the only one who would train the dog, partly because we all thought said dog – Pepper – was perfectly fine untrained. But Nick, he got up early and trained Pepper every day before school, and he trained him to bark every time I said the word "No". I have literally no idea how – I must have said it a lot – and it was only when *I* said it that the damn dog barked.' Her lips curve, a true smile now. 'Can I have crisps? No. Bark.' Evie laughs. 'Can I watch something? No. Bark.' Grace shakes her head. 'So every time I remember that, I remember how funny Nick found it, how annoyed I'd get, and I smile.'

She lifts her glass in the air, in a toast to Evie.

'And right now, I am still here, with two wonderful sons, two wonderful grandchildren, and I am sitting drinking an exceptional gin cocktail in the afternoon sun.'

'I'll cheers to that,' Evie says. She holds up her glass and then adds softly, 'To remembering more than the end.' Grace's eyes spark and she nods. Then Evie smiles, cocks her head to change the tone. 'And to gin.'

We are all a product of the choices we make. That's so true, isn't it? But we are also the product of the choices *other* people make. Because Evie wouldn't be here, sitting on this patio, if it wasn't for me dying. She wouldn't have met Nate at all, would never be talking to this amazing woman. My choice that day, to step off the pavement, has led her to this garden.

A butterfly effect. Life is a string of them, I suppose – or multiple strings, all knotted together, impossible to untangle.

And now I'm in *my* garden, the one I grew up in, and I'm about seven. I am heading out the house early one summer morning, the dew damp under my bare feet as I pad across the grass, heading for the trampoline. *My* trampoline. Mum and Dad bought it for my birthday, but the netting broke and I'm not supposed to go on it until it's fixed, because I could bounce over the edge. Instead of adhering to that rule, I am sneaking out to use it before they wake up.

I climb up, start bouncing. I grin and even though I'm trying to be quiet, so I don't get found out, I let out a whoop.

I know what's going to happen next. My adult eyes see the edge of the trampoline, the way my child eyes did not. I try to reach into my body, try to stop myself from bouncing, because I know the pain that will follow.

But I have no control over it – so I fall. And I scream, loud and piercing.

Mum comes rushing out almost instantly, the back door slamming against the wall behind her, wearing nothing but a pyjama top and knickers, her legs bare.

'Scarlett!' I am lying there, crying, clutching my arm. 'Oh my God, oh my God. What happened, what did you do? Graham! Graham, for fuck's sake get out here.'

It was a broken arm. They took me to A&E, my mum white and shaking, my dad's fingers gripping the wheel of the car too tightly. A fracture. Not enough to get a cast that everyone could sign, just a little sling – and no more trampolining until it was fixed.

I'm scowling as I come out of the A&E room, and I am told to sit on one of the chairs in the waiting room as Mum goes to sign something. Dad waits with me, but he is on the phone, telling someone that I'm okay – I'm not sure who. I am separated by one empty chair from another girl around my age, who has long dark hair spilling down her back. She's also frowning.

'Why are you here?' I ask, because I want to trump someone with my injury.

She glances at me, her eyes slightly wary. 'My mum thinks she has cholera.'

'Does she?'

'No.'

'I don't know what cholera is,' I admit.

'I don't either, but I'm sure she doesn't have it. Your arm is broken,' she says, matter-of-factly, looking at my sling.

'Yes.'

'Does it hurt?'

'No,' I say, sticking my chin in the air. Because already it's creeping in – the fact that it's my fault, that my parents were right – and I am starting to feel embarrassed by that.

'Bet it does.'

'Doesn't.'

'Does.'

'I'm Scarlett.'

The girl hesitates, like she's considering whether to tell me, whether to let me in. 'Evie,' she says finally.

We weren't at the same primary school – I was at a private one, Evie at the local one in the village – but we became friends after that, and by the time we were eleven there was no separating us. We made sure we went to the same secondary school, with me refusing to go to the school my parents wanted me to attend because Evie's mum wouldn't be able to afford it.

A butterfly effect. If it hadn't been for that decision to get up early, creep outside, and jump on the trampoline that day, I would never have met Evie. I don't know what either of us would be doing right now. Maybe I'd still be in London, still be in fashion, still be making terrible decisions about men. Evie would still have MS, obviously. She'd probably still have played the violin, even though my mum gave Evie her first one. But our lives would have been lesser somehow, I think.

My life would have been lesser, without her in it. I wish, desperately, that I had taken more time to make her realize this while I was still alive. Wish I could tell her that it wasn't one-sided. It wasn't me, sharing my brightness with Evie. We made *each other* brighter.

Chapter Twenty-Six

Evie woke, groggy and disoriented, on the sofa. She was fully clothed, a blanket draped over her, a soft pillow under her head. And she was comfortable. It was that which made her sit up quickly. This was not her sofa, this was not her flat.

One of Noah's twins bounded in at that moment — the one with the high ponytail. Did she sleep in it? Evie wondered. It seemed like an ever-present fixture. It also didn't help that she was wearing the ponytail, because she couldn't remember which one Nate had said wore it. She shoved at her own hair self-consciously; what must she look like?

'Mum says I have to check if you're awake and, if you are, I have to ask if you want a green tea.' She looked at Evie, waiting.

'Ah…'

Nate appeared in the doorway and she exchanged a look with him. 'Tell her to make Evie a milky tea with sugar,' he said to the girl.

She put her hands on her hips. 'Mum says sugar is bad for you, and you shouldn't put it in things like drinks because it's a waste.'

'Well, I reckon Mum will let Evie have sugar, as she's a guest.'

The girl gave Evie a look. 'Mum's a nutritionanist. She knows these things.'

'Does she know about the lollies I gave you guys yesterday then?' Nate asked.

'Of course.' She gave Nate a sly smile. 'I told her they were sugar-free.'

'How about some sugar-free sugar then?' Evie piped up, and the girl looked at her, assessing. She seemed to think for a moment, then gave a decisive nod.

'I think I can make that work,' she said, then bounded out the room with the same enthusiasm she'd bounded in with.

'I can't believe I passed out,' Evie said to Nate, after Twin A had left. 'I'm so sorry.' She hadn't even drunk that much, not wanting to embarrass herself if she overdid it – but Camille's gin cocktails had gone straight to her head. She'd come into the sitting room for what was only meant to be a few minutes, to sit in the quiet for a while before she made the rounds and said goodbye to everyone. And then...

'Did you sleep okay?' Nate asked.

'I guess so, considering it's... What time *is* it?' She looked around for her phone, but it was dead.

'Around nine.'

'Nine a.m.? Already? Well, that's embarrassing.' She looked up at Nate, feeling suddenly vulnerable, sitting down here, all dishevelled from the night before, while he was standing there looking all fresh. 'I better go.'

'Why?' It reminded her instantly of their kiss, his question afterwards.

I can't do it.

Why?

And although she didn't want to, she couldn't help remembering the feel of his mouth on hers, the way she'd wanted to sink into it.

'I... er...' She pulled a hand through her hair. 'Well, remember Astrid?

'Yeah. I thought her name was actually Anna?'

'It's currently up for debate. Anyway, I'm helping her with something and I promised she could come round at eleven.' Because Astrid had insisted, after yesterday, that she *got* what Evie was saying, way more than she got what the *stupid music teacher* in school was trying to say, and that they should practise every day until the concert, which was in two weeks. And as with all things Astrid, Evie had somehow ended up agreeing.

'Fair enough,' Nate said. 'I can drive you?' Then he slapped a hand to his head. 'Oh, shit, no I can't. Noah needs the car.'

'How rude of him, to want *his* car today,' she said, her voice deadpan.

'It *is* rude, isn't it? I don't know, I think they have to take the kids to hockey or something.'

'It's okay, I'll get an Uber.' She didn't want to get a train in her clothes from the night before – even though there was a perfectly innocent explanation behind it. She ordered one on her phone and then, with eight minutes to kill, she and Nate headed for the kitchen to say goodbye to Camille, who reassured her that it was totally fine she'd stayed over and that she was welcome any time. She put Evie's tea in a Thermos flask for her – 'I put two sugars in,' she added, with a wink for Natalie/Naomi – and told her to give it back to Nate, next time she saw him.

Noah, it turned out, was still in bed, hungover. 'You'll tell him thank you from me, right?' Evie said. 'And that I hope he had a good birthday?'

Nate walked her outside, and when the Uber pulled to one side a little way up the road, Evie turned to him, twisting her hands in front of her and feeling impossibly awkward.

'Thanks for inviting me.'

'Course.' Back to level ground, no questions asked, after she'd shouted at him the other day.

He was standing so close to her. So close. And this time it was her decision to step in, press her lips against his. She felt the soft curve of his mouth as he smiled against hers, and with his answering kiss, gentle this time, like he was being careful with her, she felt that long, liquid pull through her centre.

He ran his hands down her shoulders, her arms – a soft caress – and when she stepped back, just a breath away, he linked his fingers with hers. Evie bit her lip, saw him follow the movement with that intense gaze.

'How long are you staying for?' she asked. Nate frowned. 'In London, I mean.' She hadn't forgotten that he wasn't planning to stay here. That his life was the exact opposite to hers – that at some point he'd move on, while she stayed still.

'Oh, right. Until I get a commission, I suppose. I've been taking it easy, need to get pitching really.' He unlinked his hands from hers, rubbed a hand across the back of his neck.

She glanced towards the taxi waiting for her.

'Can I see you again?' Nate asked.

She looked back at him, though she found it difficult to meet his gaze. Whoever said *her* gaze was direct clearly hadn't met Nate. 'I, er, could cook you dinner?' The question was out before she'd thought better of it.

His grin was immediate. 'I'd love that. When?'

She hesitated – but she'd already started down that road, hadn't she? 'Maybe Saturday?'

'Okay, you're on.'

'I'm not a very good cook,' she said quickly.

'Okay.'

'I mean it – it'll be like the blue-soup incident in *Bridget Jones*.'

'Blue soup sounds great.'

'And I—'

But he kissed her again, lightly, and cut her off. 'I'll see you Saturday.'

She realized she was still smiling when she let herself into the flat forty minutes later. Until she put her keys down on the kitchen counter and saw the letter for Scarlett, still there, still unopened.

She was thinking of her conversation with Grace, when she picked it up. Thinking of choices, and of learning to find a place for Scarlett while somehow moving forward.

She couldn't leave the letter there indefinitely – Scarlett was not coming back to open it.

She had a flash, as she tore at the envelope seal, of a time when she'd come into her bedroom at her mum's house, around thirteen, to find Scarlett reading her diary.

What are you doing?

It was open, Eves, I'm sorry! I didn't realize what it was! But all it says is that you think Mark Cartwright is hot, which I knew anyway and—

That is not okay, Scarlett!

She'd slammed the diary shut and refused to speak to her friend for a solid two minutes, while Scarlett whined at her, *I'm sorry, I'm sorry. Let me fix it. You can read* my *diary.*

You don't even have *a diary.*

Well, I'll write a few pages of one and then you can read it. I'll make it juicy and everything.

And, obviously, Evie had ended up forgiving Scarlett, because she had been impossible not to forgive.

She slipped the piece of A4 paper out of the envelope:

Dear Miss Henderson,

We are writing to follow up from an email we sent as of 17 April and wish to know if you would like to proceed with your offer on 32 Four Acres, the property in Borough Market? We have received your reference check, and the occupancy is due to start 18 May. Could you please get in touch at your earliest convenience to confirm that you will be moving in, and to set up the direct debit? If we do not hear from you, we will have to put the property back on the market.

Kind regards,
Kate Fisher

Garrett Whitelock Letting Agents

Evie stared at the letter.

Borough Market.

That was where Scarlett had been, the day she died. This explained why she was nowhere near work, why she wasn't where she was supposed to be.

She hadn't told Evie. She hadn't told her that she was looking at another flat. That she'd made an offer, for Christ's sake. Evie was gripping the letter too tightly now and she lowered it slowly, trying to let this new knowledge settle through her.

Scarlett had died that day because she'd gone to look at this flat, in Borough Market. And she'd lied to Evie about it. She'd lied about the fact that she wasn't only leaving the flat that day – she was planning to leave it for good. Even before their argument the night before, she must have been planning to go. Go and leave Evie behind.

Chapter Twenty-Seven

Oh, Evie. She has set the letter down now, and her movements are stiff as she crosses the kitchen to get herself a glass of water. She stands there for a moment, bracing both hands on the sink, the tap still on, water flowing.

I should have told her at the time – I know that, honestly. I was going to when I got back from work, the night before I died. But then things blew up and, well...

I'm there now, on that evening, letting myself into the flat, the last time I'll ever do so. The key gets stuck in the lock and I swear. I am impatient to be inside, as I am generally impatient to do everything. The doorknob is smooth and cold in my hand as I twist it and, though I didn't at the time, now I relish the feel of it on my skin, because it's the last time I'll feel it, the last time I'll be this side of the door, outside going in.

Evie is standing in the kitchen, wearing fluffy socks and that fucking holey cardigan, when I get in. She does not look good. I know her relapse was officially 'over' a week ago, but she's not fully recovered from it. Each time she has a relapse there's the worry that one of the new symptoms will decide to stick around, instead of fading at the end of it. Like the tremor, and the stiff muscles. She'd been struggling with balance more and more during the latest relapse but, thankfully, that seems to have receded a bit.

Evie glances over at me, from where she's standing next to the toaster. 'Good day?' she asks.

'Yeah, all right.' I've been getting ready for the meeting with the investors tomorrow all day, and I know there are a million things on my mind right now. The flat-viewing, Jason, my idea for the label.

Bread pops up out of the toaster, and Evie puts the two slices on the wooden chopping board that my mum bought me – my last present from her. Suddenly I feel a rush of love for that chopping board. 'Toast for dinner?' I ask.

'Yep,' Evie says, now buttering it. 'One of my five a day.'

I dump my crocodile handbag down by the front door – where did it end up? I wonder. 'Five pieces of toast a day?' I ask. 'Ambitious.'

'Yeah, but you know me. I'm *all* about ambition.' Her voice holds a trace of bitterness. She turns, leans back against the counter and waves her toast at me. 'It's all about the small goals in life, Scar.' She takes a bite. 'Have you eaten? Want some toast?'

'I grabbed something on the way home.' I cross to the kitchen, leaning against the counter opposite her, the one that separates kitchen and living room. 'How was *your* day?'

'Oh, thrilling,' Evie says over a mouthful of toast. 'Full of adrenaline and high stakes.' Her words are slurring. I know she hates that.

I tap my fingernails – which I had done today, ready for tomorrow – against the countertop. 'I think we should go back to Ireland this summer. A long weekend or something. What do you reckon?' I'd been practising what to say to her on the way home, I remember.

'Maybe,' Evie says, starting on her second piece of toast now.

'Maybe?'

'Yes, Scar, maybe.' She shakes her head. 'I can't plan that far ahead, you know that. Because I don't know what will happen, do I? I don't want to be stuck in Ireland when I have a bad relapse.' There it is, the bitterness again. It's particularly bad this time. Usually she can claw back from it, get a handle on it. I'm not sure why this time hit her so hard – and I realize now that I never asked. I asked her how she was feeling, if there was anything I could do, all of that. But I didn't ask her why this time was worse, why she felt more down about it.

In hindsight, I probably should have clocked the bitterness a bit more. Probably should have realized that *now* was not the time to push. But then patience isn't exactly my strong suit, is it?

'*Stuck* in Ireland?' I say incredulously. 'Evie, you're stuck here! And Ireland's hardly the bloody Nigerian desert.'

Evie finishes her toast, chews slowly. She doesn't lash out at me – not yet. Instead I can tell she's trying to keep her voice calm. 'You know what I mean. I can't predict how I'll be doing, so being stuck here is better than being stuck somewhere I don't know, *Can't predict*. It would be hell for anyone, I reckon, not knowing how bad it was going to get in the future, but for Evie in particular.

Maybe I should have been more sympathetic to that. Instead I say, my voice a bit biting, 'Fine, then *I* don't want to be stuck here.' I take my jacket off and throw it on the sofa. 'Eves, I can't stay here, cooped up like this, it's driving me mad.'

Evie gives me a look. 'You're not stuck here – you can go anywhere. You *do* go anywhere and everywhere.

'But I don't,' I say, my voice a little pleading, 'because I also want to be here for you, want to spend time with you and—'

'What?' Snappier, now. And unsurprisingly so. When did I decide to make her feel *blamed*? I'm not sure I meant to – I think I'm just tired and distracted, and I want to try and motivate her to do something different with her life. But I am clearly going about it the wrong way. 'You want to spend time with me, but only if we're off doing something exciting?'

'That's not what I'm saying,' I huff, even though clearly it is.

Evie crosses her arms. 'I don't *want* to go out doing things. I can't,' she corrects.

'You had it right the first time – you don't want to.'

'Well, so what if that's true?' She throws her arms in the air. 'So what if I don't want to do what you wish to do, don't go to the parties any more, talk to endless people who prattle on about nothing? So what if I'm being more discerning over when I want to make the effort? I am happier at home, Scarlett – don't you get that?'

'But you're *not* happy!' As if I have some sort of authority on happiness.

'I thought you got it,' Evie says, her voice nearly a shout now. 'I thought you understood that I can't do the things I used to be able to. I have a disease, don't you get that? You said it was fine if I was happier at home, if I didn't have the energy to keep' – she waves a hand in the air as she thinks – 'putting myself on show.'

'But that's when I thought you'd…'

Evie raises her eyebrows, an almost disdainful look. 'I'd what, Scar?' And I think we both know what I was about to say. I thought she'd change her mind. Thought she'd get over it. Something to that effect.

Luckily I do not say this. Instead I cross to my handbag, fumble around in it, then turn back to her, holding up the leaflets. 'Look, I picked these up.' I hold them out to her and, when she glares at them instead of taking them, I put them down on the counter:

**MS and your emotions: understanding
and dealing with your feelings**

Complementary and alternative medicine

**Mindfulness as a way to cope with
a long-term condition.**

Bright and colourful, they take up the space between us.

'I thought it was up to *me* how to manage it.' Her voice is icy calm – the calm before the storm.

'It is,' I say with another huff. 'I just thought—'

'And who are you,' she snaps, erupting, 'to judge *my* decisions?'

Something hot flashes through me. 'This isn't about Jason.'

'No, of course not.' Evie's tone is scathing now. 'Because it's totally fine for you to make a judgement on how I live my life, but *your* decisions—'

'But you're not *living* your life, are you, Evie?'

She reaches for her water glass and, because I know what's about to happen, I see it: the way her hand trembles in the air. She's moving quickly, though – quicker than usual, fuelled by her anger at me – so she doesn't catch it, the way she usually does. She goes to grab the glass, picks it up, only for her hand to spasm and the glass to slip from her grip.

It explodes on the lino flooring like a firework, shards glinting as they fly.

The two of us say nothing, staring at it. Until Evie, her face tight, makes a stiff movement towards the cupboard under the sink where we keep the dustpan and brush.

'I'll do it,' I say quickly.

'It's fine,' Evie says, through gritted teeth.

'But I—'

'I said it's fine, okay!'

That was it. The last we said on the matter. That was the last real conversation I had with her, because I'm not sure the next morning counts. And yes, there is a part of me that still gets it, what I said. Because she *was* closing in on herself, and I was frustrated: with her and with myself, for not being able to do anything about it. And *she* was clearly frustrated with *me* – because she was right, too. I kept living my life, moving my way up in the world, and I can see how it might have looked like I was leaving her here, behind.

That's what she'll hang on to, isn't it? Because of the fucking letter. She'll think of this argument, think of what I said: that I didn't want to be *stuck* here, with her. I didn't mean it. Not like that. I just wanted her to see that there was still so much out there that she could do, could enjoy. I wanted *both* of us to move on, to move upwards – I wanted us to do that together. But I'll never get the chance to tell Evie that.

Chapter Twenty-Eight

'I can't get it right!' Astrid lowered her violin in frustration, made a slashing movement with her bow.

'Well,' Evie said from her position at the desk chair, watching Astrid play by the window, 'unless you're the next Vengerov, I doubt you'll get everything right the first time.'

Astrid gave her a sour look, and it was so brilliantly teenage that it made Evie want to grin. 'Am I supposed to know who that is?'

'Maybe. If you want to take music seriously. Hc was a Russian violinist. A child prodigy.'

Astrid scowled but said nothing. She'd been at it for an hour, and Evie could tell she was getting tired; some of the notes were coming out squeaky and she kept glaring at the music sheet. They were trying to modify one of Astrid's favourite compositions – because actually she was right, why not give it a go? – and Evie thought they were on to something. Not completely unique, but different enough to add a little quirk, a bit of verve.

Astrid sighed. 'I'll never be able to do this professionally, will I? I didn't start early enough. I'm not good enough.'

Evie hesitated. She didn't want to offer false promises. In the end she settled for honesty. 'I don't know,' she said. 'It's difficult, to make a living from it. But that absolutely doesn't mean you shouldn't try. And really, right now, if you love it, then that's the reason to do it.'

'I *do* love it,' Astrid said fiercely, and Evie nodded.

'Hold on to that while you practise, and try not to worry so much about the other stuff.' She'd lost that herself, Evie realized. She'd never lost her love for music – she didn't think she *could* lose that. She'd tried to, after she came to the conclusion that she couldn't play any more, because she'd thought it would be less painful if she stopped loving it. But music, and the violin especially, was a part of her soul, and there was no shaking that. Still, somewhere along the line, before she'd been forced to stop, she'd begun to play for a reason rather than for the love for it. 'Right,' she said decisively, 'I reckon we should leave it at that for today.'

'But I—'

Evie held up a hand. 'You have to go anyway, because I've got someone coming round for dinner.' Her stomach was churning at the thought of it, even though she'd prepared the lasagne – because who *didn't* like lasagne? – last night, not wanting to be watched while she cooked, not wanting the fatigue, the stiffness, to hit her while she was supposed to be walking around the kitchen, all sexy. And probably barefoot. Wasn't that what sexy kitchen goddesses did: swan around barefoot? Damn it, she should have painted her toenails.

Astrid's eyes turned sharp. 'Who's coming round?'

'None of your business,' Evie said, prodding her in the ribs.

'It's the sexy journalist, isn't it?'

Evie just rolled her eyes, mimicking the way Astrid did it. 'Good work today,' she said as she walked her to the front door. Astrid sort of shrugged at the compliment. 'You too,' Evie murmured, tracing one finger down her violin.

Astrid shook her head. 'You're so weird.'

Evie laughed. 'Only about violins.'

Astrid lingered, not opening the door, and bit her lip as she looked down at her violin.

'You'll do well, you know,' Evie said. 'At the concert.'

'I want it to be *perfect*, though.'

'That's a lot of pressure. To be perfect. And you haven't had as long as everyone else to get ready for it.'

'I know, but…' She tailed off, went quiet.

'But what?'

'Everyone will be watching,' she said gruffly, scuffing her toe on the carpet. Evie wasn't sure, but she could have sworn there was a slight inflection on the word *everyone*.

'Well, everyone else can't play a musical instrument and play it well. You can.'

'Some people can. The girl in the orchestra, the one I told you about. She plays the cello so well.' A blush crept up Astrid's neck, but before Evie could respond to that, she looked up. 'You'll be there, right? At the concert?'

'Course. I've got it in my diary.'

'Okay. Good.' Astrid opened the door – and revealed Nate, standing there with one hand raised, about to knock. She laughed delightedly. 'It *is* the sexy journalist!'

Nate offered her his easy grin. 'As nicknames go, I'll take that.'

Evie's heart gave an extra-large thump and she felt her pulse surge against her wrists. But she frowned. 'You're early,' she said, a touch of accusation in her voice.

Nate checked his watch. 'You said seven, right? It's ten past. I'm actually fashionably late.'

Astrid glanced at Evie. 'Oops. Soz.'

Soz? Really? Who actually said that?

'Well, have fun!' Astrid gave a little salute with her bow, then strutted across the hallway to her flat.

'You going to let me in?' Nate asked. 'Or is it like a cool, quirky hallway dinner?'

'Sorry.' God, why did she feel so flustered? It was only dinner, for Christ's sake. 'Come in.' She stepped aside, shut the door after him. He was clutching a rather bulky-looking package, along with a bottle of wine.

He held up the wine first. 'White,' he said. 'What with it being summer and all.' It felt too warm in the flat, she realized. It always got stuffy in here over the summer – she should have opened a window.

'Thanks, I'll put it in the fridge.' She did exactly that, taking out the cold bottle she'd bought earlier and filling up two glasses. Why wasn't there a mirror in the kitchen? Suddenly that felt like a serious shortcoming. She hadn't even changed, for God's sake.

He'd followed her to the kitchen and was standing on the other side of the kitchen counter, the one that acted as a barrier between kitchen and living room. She held out a glass to him and they clinked glasses. His gaze stayed on hers the entire time, and in the end she was the one to tear hers away. Was she blushing? She was blushing, wasn't she? *Get a bloody grip, Evie.*

'I, er, made lasagne – is that okay?'

'Perfect.' He took a sip of his wine, set it down on the kitchen countertop. Then he held up the package he'd brought with him. 'This is for you.' But he didn't let go of it.

Evie raised her eyebrows. 'Traditionally you hand over a gift when you give it to someone.'

He didn't smile, though, and his gaze flicked between her and the present, wrapped roughly in brown paper. 'I…' He swallowed, his Adam's apple bobbing. And his nerves made her own prick. 'Listen, I don't know how this will go down.'

'Okay,' Evie said slowly, putting down her wine.

'If you don't like it, I can return it. Burn it. Whatever. I just… it was sort of an impulse decision, and then it arrived and, well, I thought I should at least *see* if you wanted it.'

'Nate,' Evie said firmly. 'Giving me the context only works if I know what it is.'

'Right. Right.' He frowned down at the parcel, then handed it over to her. The brown paper crinkled beneath her fingers as she took it. It was soft, like there was fabric inside. Did he buy her a scarf or something? Will bought her a scarf for her birthday, the first year they were together. It was dark blue with over-the-top smiling sunshines on it, and though she'd worn it when she was with him to save his feelings, it was now confined to the back of the wardrobe – smiling sunshines weren't really her thing, she and Scarlett had agreed. But she didn't have Nate down as the scarf-buying type.

She tore at the paper, saw something wrapped in light-green tissue paper, a single round sticker keeping it in place. Her fingers lightened as she opened the second layer, and she felt Nate's gaze on her face the whole time.

When she saw what was inside, her breath caught. She pulled it out in one fluid movement, the fabric swishing, the tissue paper that had been holding it fluttering to the floor.

It was Scarlett's dress. The one she'd designed for Evie, before she died. Made from the drawing that she had not been able to bring herself to give Jason yet.

She ran a hand down the deep-green fabric, touching the contours of the dress, and felt her eyes spark. She looked at Nate. 'How?' she breathed. 'How is this possible?'

He ran a hand across the back of his neck. 'I… I took a picture of it, when I was here last, and I… I told you: it was an impulse decision, one of those things I did without thinking.'

'Really?' Evie said on a shaky breath. 'That's not like you.'

He smiled, and she could see relief course through his body. 'Well. Anyway, I know a guy—'

'Of course you do.'

'And he put me in touch with someone who might be able to make it. I figured it might, I don't know, give you something to help with…' He shook his head. 'I don't know. It felt like a good idea at the time, anyway. It was right after you told me about her thirtieth birthday, do you remember?'

'I remember,' Evie said softly. She looked down at the dress again, tried to swallow away the tightness in her throat.

'So… You're not mad?'

She frowned slightly, at the fact that he had to check. She supposed that, despite spending years trying *not* to get mad, she'd lashed out at him a fair few times since meeting him. 'I'm not mad,' she said firmly. She looked up, met his gaze. 'Thank you.'

Scarlett was going to move out. She was going to leave me. The thought pierced her mind, despite herself. But she decided not to tell him. Because what Nate's mum had said to her at the barbecue was right – she couldn't change what had happened. She didn't know what Scarlett had been thinking or why she'd been planning to make that choice, but regardless, she didn't want to let it dampen what Scarlett had meant to her. It didn't change how much she'd loved her; it didn't mean that their friendship hadn't still been wonderful and essential.

She didn't want to bring up what Scarlett had been doing at Borough Market that day, either. Somehow Evie felt like this gift, it was both for her *and* Scarlett – like Nate had known that Scarlett would have loved the fact that her design got to live on, after she died. Immortalizing her. So it wasn't that Scarlett was being ignored in this moment –

far from it – but pointing out what she had been doing that day would only bring them back to that moment again. The moment she stepped off the pavement to help him. And that would inevitably put up a wall between them, if only a glass one. And really Evie had either decided to forgive him, decided to accept that it was an accident, or she hadn't.

So she said none of that and, holding the dress as carefully as she could, she moved out of the kitchen and laid it down on the back of the sofa. Then she turned to Nate, stepped towards him and framed his face with her hands. 'Thank you,' she said again and pressed her lips lightly to his.

Nate caught one of her hands in his as she eased back, and her skin thrummed with the contact. 'I didn't do it to get in your good books.'

'I know that.'

His other hand came up to her shoulder, ran down the length of her arm in that way of his. She moved her hand towards his hair, but her hand shook, breaking the steadiness she felt. She scowled, shook it out and he reached up to catch it again. 'Don't,' he murmured. Then he lifted her hand, kissed it. She could feel herself holding her breath as he looked at her. 'It doesn't matter.' He tucked her hair behind her ears, then grinned, changing the tone. 'I can pretend it's me making you feel that anyway. It'll do wonders for my ego.'

She laughed, a tiny bit breathlessly. 'It's a little bit of that, I'm sure.'

'Only a little?'

She gave him a teasing punch on the arm. 'Cocky, aren't you?'

'Always. That's kind of my thing.'

They were grinning at each other, but he still held one hand in hers, the other now resting lightly on her shoulder. And she was aware of quite how close their bodies were, how easy it would be to lean in, slide her arms around him. Her heart started pounding, more alive than she'd felt it in a while, and she felt his mood shift at the same time as hers.

He leaned towards her, but halted, frowning. A question. So she closed the distance and kissed him, felt his arms come round her, lifting her to her toes. She entwined her arms around his neck, pulling him closer, her whole body vibrating with his touch.

But then he pulled away. 'Wait, wait,' he said breathlessly, 'we don't have to – I mean, this isn't why I came round.'

Evie nodded, trying to get her own breathing under control. 'I know that.'

'I just… I wanted to spend time with you, and I didn't bring the dress to—'

She kissed him once, firmly. 'Nate. I know that.' Her turn to hesitate. 'Unless you don't want to?'

'Is that some kind of trick question?'

She felt herself flush and looked away, down to the floor. 'Well, I don't know, you might feel… weird, being with someone who has—'

'Evie.' He gave her arms a squeeze to emphasize his point and she looked back at him. 'You're being ridiculous.'

'Way to seduce me,' she muttered, and he laughed.

'You are being ridiculous,' he repeated. He moved his hands to her waist and pressed a kiss to each corner of her mouth, then lightly on her neck. She felt her body go tight – not tight like it usually did, but expectant. Waiting.

'I know I don't understand how it changed your life,' Nate murmured. 'But when I spend time with you, I don't see someone who has an illness. I see someone who is kind and clever, and more vibrant than you give yourself credit for.' He rested his forehead against hers, and their breathing slowed into one rhythm. 'And I have literally never wanted anything more in my life.'

Her stomach swooped. 'Well, okay then. I just thought I should check.'

Then finally he was kissing her properly, pulling her to him, running his hands up her back, underneath her T-shirt, so that she could feel his hands on her bare skin. And this time, when she trembled, it was *all* because of him.

Chapter Twenty-Nine

Evie curled up on the sofa in the living room, tapping her fingers against her mug of tea and trying not to keep glancing obsessively towards her bedroom. She'd pulled on the first clothes she could find – an old T-shirt and pyjama shorts – because she didn't want to wake Nate up.

Nate. Asleep. In her room. Naked.

But she couldn't relax, worrying about how she should act when he eventually came out. And she was regretting the quick change, because she didn't exactly look sexy, did she? And who was to say he would *want* to find her here waiting for him, when he got up? Well, obviously she'd be here, it was her flat, but they'd never explicitly discussed him staying over, it had just sort of happened.

She felt a pang for Scarlett, who would probably have delighted in this – Evie having a guy in her bed. She could imagine her friend's wicked grin as she came into the kitchen in the morning, the way she'd tease Evie, then blink all innocently at Nate. But then Evie's stomach lurched because it was *Nate*, not some random guy that Scarlett would be teasing – and she'd only met Nate because Scarlett had died. Guilt fell like pebbles in her stomach, and she twisted her mug between her hands. What would Scarlett be thinking, if she was watching all this? Would she hate Evie for it? *Should* she hate her for it? Should she feel guilty about this?

'Hey.' Evie jolted and looked over to see Nate coming towards her, his voice husky from sleep.

'Hey,' Evie said. No, too high-pitched. *Jesus, woman, control your voice.*

'Have you been up long?'

'No, not long.' Was it awkward? It felt awkward. Did *he* feel awkward? Did he regret it? Did *she* regret it?

No, she decided firmly. She didn't. Things would be different if Scarlett was alive, but she wasn't, and Evie had to deal with that. And Nate… Well, it was kind of hard to regret something that had made every other orgasm in her life, which was *not* that many, look like…

Nate came to perch on the edge of the sofa, and Evie tried to ignore the urge to tug at her T-shirt. 'You put music on,' he stated.

Evie felt heat blossom around her collarbone. 'You said you couldn't sleep without it,' she said. 'And you fell asleep before me.' Had fallen asleep with his arms around her, his body pressed against hers, legs tangled together. It was why she'd woken so early, the heat of him triggering a slight spasm, the way heat always tended to make some of her symptoms worse. It had been worth it, though. In that moment she had felt safe, and content, and wanted. 'I didn't want you to wake without it,' she added. Not after what he'd told her.

She didn't add that it was the first time she'd played music out loud in this flat, as opposed to listening on her

260

headphones, in a long time. That it had been a long time since she'd allowed someone to share it with her.

'Thank you.' He leaned towards her, kissed her forehead. He grinned at her as he pulled back, changing the tone so instantly in a way that seemed natural to him. It was a slight front, she was starting to think. Not completely – he *was* relatively carefree, jokey, impulsive. But there was also something deeper there, which came out in flashes. 'Think I had another reason to sleep well last night, though.'

Heat licked her insides, from the way he was looking at her. 'Ah, do you want anything?' He smirked and she huffed out a laugh. 'As in, coffee? Tea?'

'Coffee would be great, thanks.' She got up, went the long way round the sofa to the kitchen, feeling it was safer not to pass right by him, and he came with her, leaning against the counter as she flicked the kettle on.

'So I was thinking we could go somewhere today,' he began. 'If you're up for it. I know someone who—'

'Actually,' she interrupted, 'I have somewhere I'd like to take you.' The idea had been playing around her mind this morning – though she hadn't worked out if she was going to ask him until just now. 'You're always taking me places – so let me return the favour.'

He came up to her, ran his hands down her arms. 'Mysterious. I like it.'

'You know me,' Evie said wryly. 'Queen of mystery.'

His hand moved to her neck, his thumb tracing circles on her skin, sending a shiver of pleasure down her spine.

'Maybe you're more mysterious than you give yourself credit for.'

She tried to keep the tone light. 'In comparison to you? Because that's not hard.'

He smiled as he bent his head towards her, kissed her. Something *else* was hard, pressing against her, and she felt an answering pulse in her core. He tasted of mint and the fact that he'd brushed his teeth, the fact that he'd planned it, made it even more sexy, somehow.

She'd assumed that MS would mean the end of sex like this, the end of sex where she really *wanted* it. It was what had happened with Will and maybe it still would happen, in the long run. Maybe it was just because it was new and exciting and… She gasped as Nate kissed her neck, as his hands caressed her hip, her waist.

'Stop overthinking,' he whispered against her lips. And when he picked her up, when she wrapped her legs around him, locking herself in place, she did stop thinking. She stopped thinking and allowed herself just to feel.

Evie took in a deep breath of forest air as she walked. Sunlight filtered through the leaves above, creating pockets of light where the dust sparkled. It was warm, the trees providing much-needed shade, and though she rarely did this any more – walked simply for the pleasure of it, because it inevitably became difficult and tiring – she felt if not her body, then a deeper part of her relaxing into the rhythm of it.

It had taken them over an hour to get here on the train,

once they'd hit Paddington. An hour when they'd sat opposite each other, chatting about nonsense or looking out of the window, watching as London eased into countryside. An hour when her knee had rested against Nate's through the fabric of her long skirt and his jeans, and she'd tried not to think of the way that casual touch was making her body spark.

He hadn't asked her where they were going, but that didn't exactly surprise her. It was a pattern they'd fallen into somewhere along the way – trusting each other enough to go along with something, without any information beforehand. And now they were walking through the woods, the wind rustling, the mud still soft in places where the light never reached it, the sound of a stream trickling in the background.

'I found this place by accident,' Evie was telling him. 'But it's amazing because it sounds so musical, don't you think?' She stopped for a moment, so they could both listen to the way the trees creaked – the way they *sang* – the breeze adding background noise as it rustled through. 'It's actually a thing,' she continued as they started walking again. 'Scar and I looked it up: it's to do with the combination of trees here, the types of wood or whatever, so it makes it sound like they're singing to one another. Like they're communicating.'

'Maybe they are,' Nate said. 'They have networks, trees. They can send nutrients to each other when one is in need, or whatever, can hear distress signals from others if one is chopped down.'

'Really?'

'Apparently. Not that I claim to be an expert.'

She went quiet. It felt a little sad to her, the trees communicating with each other the only way they could: slow, quiet. She reached out, ran a hand down the bark of the nearest trees. They lived for so long. But they were fragile too – just like everything else.

Do you get bored here? she asked it silently. *Do you ever wish for something different? Do you feel it, as disease takes hold – do you know it will be the end?*

'Anyway,' she carried on, 'that's not the only thing that's special about this place; people come here to play music, too. Hence the musical forest.'

'Have you ever? Come here to play?'

She paused, then shook her head. She used to want to, but had long since given up on that idea. She should bring Astrid here, she thought suddenly. She'd love it – playing in the wild, like no one was listening, whilst always knowing that there *might* still be someone listening. She thought again of the trees. Maybe it made them less lonely, listening to the people who came here to play. Maybe it was *that*, and not the scientific reason of different types of trees in the wind or whatever, that made the forest sing.

Nate took her hand, linking his fingers with hers, and it felt so easy, so natural. Then they heard it: a flute, somewhere in the forest. Nate's eyes went bright, looking delighted.

Evie grinned. 'Told you.' She and Scarlett had been driving that day, and had stopped the car because Scarlett had been desperate for a wee. But then they'd gone for a walk and discovered the secret of the forest.

'I should write a piece about it,' Nate mused. Evie bit her lip and he glanced down at her. 'Sorry.' He squeezed her hand. 'I won't.'

She nodded, grateful for the immediate understanding. Because if too many people came, if it became a tourist attraction, it would be ruined.

'Nick would have loved this,' Nate said – and Evie clocked that it was the first time he'd brought up his name since they'd argued. She said nothing, allowing him to talk. 'He was always the first one volunteering to take the dog on a walk. He loved the dog, first and foremost, but I think he also liked the excuse for the alone-time, spending it outdoors. I think… I'm not saying this was the only reason, I know depression is more complicated than that. But I think being locked up, for however little time, without being able to be alone outside, it sort of… broke something in him.'

Evie touched her free hand to the back of his in comfort. 'Maybe, wherever he is, he is outside now. Energy can't just disappear, right? So maybe he is somewhere he loves – out here, part of the trees.' It was the type of thing that sometimes sounds stupid, said out loud, but Nate nodded and she sensed she'd been right to say it.

They came to a stop by a little stream. Nate, seeming to sense that Evie needed to rest, sat down without asking her on the rocky bank, then slipped his shoes off, to put his feet in the water.

Evie dropped her head onto his shoulder, felt his arm come around her. And in that moment she felt as though life was offering her up a little slice of contentment, despite everything.

She thought about that word – *broke*. It *broke* something in him. And she admitted to herself that's how she'd been thinking of herself. She'd been convincing herself that she was *broken*. But maybe she wasn't quite as broken as she thought she was. And even if she was, well. Broken things didn't always stay broken, did they?

Chapter Thirty

I am pulled to Evie in the middle of the night. I don't know when, exactly, but there's a softening of the black edges, one that seems to come just before the sunrise in summer.

Evie is asleep in Nate's arms, her dark hair spilling over her shoulders, summer pyjamas on. He's still wearing his jeans and they are both lying on top of the duvet, like they fell asleep without really meaning to, like they've had one of those nights when you stay up talking.

I am there the second before Nate jerks awake, suddenly, as if pulled from a nightmare. He blinks, looks around him. First at Evie, then around the room. Then at Evie again. His brow furrows, like he's confused about where he is – or what woke him. There's no music, I realize. Is he really that dependent on it?

He shifts his arm away from Evie slowly, trying not to wake her, and slips his phone out of his jeans pocket. The battery is low – bar on red – but it has enough power to check his messages. One from his brother. **Going well with Evie, I take it??**

And one from his mum. **Noah says you're not at home and I can't get hold of you, are you okay?**

He replies to his mum, not to Noah. Of course she'd be

worried, I realize with a lurch. One of her sons took his own life.

Nate gets up, looks around for something – his top, presumably – and Evie stirs. He freezes, looking at her as she rubs a hand over her face, shifts into a half-sitting position.

'What time is it?' she murmurs, her voice thick with sleep.

'Five-thirty,' Nate answers.

Evie frowns. 'Five-thirty? Are you...' She shakes her head, props herself further up on her elbows. 'What are you doing up at five-thirty?'

His shoulders hunch with guilt. 'I've got to... My brother is worried about where I am.' But no. It's not his brother, but his mother who is worried – a half truth. What's the real truth, Nate? What are you thinking here? I try to throw my energy towards him, to somehow get inside his mind, but I might as well be trying to set the whole flat on fire, for all the good it does me.

'Oh,' Evie says. 'Okay.' She wraps her arms around herself, and Nate hovers in the doorway. I feel a spark of hope. I think he *wants* Evie to ask him to stay. *Say it, Evie. Fight for him.*

'I should go,' Nate says again. Still not moving, though.

'Okay,' Evie repeats, in that same too-even tone. Too even because of all the practice she's had, shoving her feelings down. Neither of them says anything for a moment, both of them looking at each other in the half darkness. 'What are you doing later?' She blurts it out, like she's been working up the courage to ask.

Nate hesitates. 'Er… not really sure yet.'

'Okay, well, it's just that I have an appointment. A doctor's appointment,' she adds, and though it's too dark to tell for sure, I hear the flush in her voice. She won't like it, I know, highlighting this vulnerability, calling attention to her MS. But I also see it for what it is: a test.

Nate's pause is a beat too long – and in that beat I know: he's about to fuck it up. 'Oh,' he says eventually. He clears his throat. 'Right.'

He rubs a hand across the back of his neck. Seriously, what the hell is he thinking right now? He's freaking out about something, clearly. His feelings for Evie? Does he have them? I feel sure he does, but maybe he doesn't want to get dragged in any further – doesn't want to be the one she depends on. It's changed, hasn't it? It's no longer him helping someone through a difficult time, no longer him trying to *make up* for his role in my death; it's something more now. And it would ruin his lifestyle, wouldn't it? All the travelling around, the carefree, happy-go-lucky attitude. Can't do that so easily with another person weighing you down – especially someone who needs security. Prick!

But the thing is, as much as I want to hate him bitterly for it, I can only manage about 80 per cent. Because of the damned dress. The fact that he thought of it; the fact he did it for Evie and, maybe, a little bit for me too. And because a part of me thinks that, despite what he's portraying to

Evie right now, he wants to be there. But maybe he doesn't know how – not yet.

Evie is the one to close it off. She doesn't push it any further, doesn't actually *ask* Nate to go with her. I know why: it would be too much to put her heart on the line there, and do you know what? I get it. After Jason, I get it. 'Well, I suppose I'll see you later then,' she says and she shifts to lie on her side, facing away from him.

No. I hate this. I don't want to see her close off like this again. *Stay, Nate!* But he doesn't listen to me. He turns and pads out of the room. Evie doesn't turn to look. Doesn't see the way he waits, the way his eyes linger on her for one moment more, before he leaves completely.

And now it is me lying in bed, at Jason's Soho flat, a sheet pulled up around my waist, my top half bare. I'm over the self-conscious stage with Jason – and really it's hard to be self-conscious, given the way he looks at me. This is our usual haunt now; our entire relationship has basically played out within these four walls. He hasn't been back to my flat, at first because I hadn't wanted to take him there, too embarrassed to show him where I lived in comparison to his place, and then because he always claimed that Soho was easier – which it was, but still. He hasn't met Evie, or any of my other friends. And he most definitely has not met my parents; they don't even know he exists. It felt exciting, like I had him all to myself. But in hindsight it was perhaps a little isolating. He didn't do it deliberately to cut me off or anything – he had his own reasons – but that was the effect, whether or not I realized it at the time.

Jason's getting ready, half dressed as he moves around the bedroom.

'Why do you have to leave so early?' I am a master of the pout and I use it now, shamelessly.

'I told you, I've got this shoot. And then the party later.' He pulls on a shirt, starts buttoning it, covering up all that muscle.

'Well, how about I come to the party with you?' I'm feeling bold, after the nights we've spent together – last night in particular. I feel all loose and liquid, and I swear I can still feel it in my toes.

'You can't, you know that.'

A pause, then, 'Will Helen be there?' Helen – his wife. A name I don't bring up very often. I'm not sure I'd even said it out loud, before this point. Like saying it would bring her to life.

His fingers fumble one of the shirt buttons. 'No, she won't.'

It hangs between us. It's a party where there might be press: people might take photos, share on social media if nothing else. People will gossip, for sure. And now I've put it out there. It's been four months since we first slept together, and I'm putting it out there.

I know. He knows I know. There is no point hiding it, even though my stomach lurches and I feel sick at the confirmation on his face. Would I take it back? I was happier when I could pretend. But that's the point – it was pretend, wasn't it? It was only ever pretend.

Jason gives up on the shirt buttons and crosses the bedroom to get to me. 'I'm going to leave her, Scarlett.'

He sits on the edge of the bed and reaches for my hand. I give it to him without question. 'When this started, I... I wasn't thinking. You were just *there*, so vibrant, and I didn't think it through.' Another lurch – confirmation that he didn't take it seriously, that he was lying to me because he thought I'd be another notch, a fling, barely worth having a conversation with.

'But I love you,' Jason says, almost a growl. The words ripple through me as he pulls me towards him. The sheet falls down further, but his eyes stay resolutely on my face. 'I love you,' he repeats firmly.

It's the first time he's said it – before *I've* said it. Was he doing it deliberately, saying it to me then? I don't think so. Not completely anyway, because whatever else, however foolhardy, I do believe he loved me.

'I want to be with you,' he continues and he brings a hand to my face, rubbing his thumb softly over my cheek. 'But it's complicated. I have to find the right moment, and my wife, she's stressed at the moment. She runs a travel business and it's failing, and it's not the right time.'

I cover his hand on my face with my own. It's so warm, so solid. 'Well,' I say and my voice is steady, 'maybe we shouldn't see each other then. Until it is the right time.' Because now that it's out there, now that I can't pretend, I have to have this conversation.

His hand drops from my face. 'I don't want to lose you.'

'Then pick me,' I say fiercely. Determined enough – and *sure* enough – that I am willing to put my heart on the line, like Evie cannot. I hook my arms around his neck and Jason brings his hands to my waist, almost like he can't control it. He lays his forehead against mine, closes his eyes. I close my eyes too. 'Pick me,' I whisper again. And I felt sure, in that moment, that he *would*. That he couldn't look at me the way he did, couldn't tell me that he loved me with such conviction, and not leave her for me.

It's pathetic, isn't it, that I still want to know? I want to know if that's what he was going to tell me, the day I died. If he would have picked me, in the end.

Chapter Thirty-One

Evie sat in the corner of the café, checking the time on her phone for the third time. Her mum was now fifteen minutes late. Which would be fine – rude, maybe, but fine – if she wasn't meeting her on a lunch break. She had to be back in the office in half an hour, and Henry was the master of clock-watching. She was going to have to start working from home again soon. It wasn't only the fatigue that set in later in the day, but the sheer *mundaneness* of it. Why had she never fully realized quite how boring her job was? The thought of working from home, though, was not filling her with much joy, either: endless days alone. Where exactly 'home' would be, she wasn't yet sure. She'd handed in her notice to her landlord, finally, and had two viewings this evening, where she'd be living with another three people – if they liked her enough to let her move in. New place, new people. Same job. Same city. Same disease.

She frowned to herself. *That's not helping, is it, Evie?* At least she'd taken some positive steps. It had been Nate walking out on her that had done it. Not quite the morning after, but… the morning after the morning after? The way she'd asked him to come with her to the doctor's, something that Scarlett used to do, and he'd let it slide past. And he hadn't been in touch with her since. No calls, no texts. And she wouldn't be the one to call him, to beg him to see her. He clearly didn't want to let her drag him down; wanted to get on, live his life. And so, fine – maybe she should be doing some of that herself.

Her phone buzzed from its position on the table. It was probably her mum, cancelling on her because some sort of illness had come on during the Tube ride or something. Or maybe, even after she'd given herself a talking-to on that very subject, it would be Nate. Texting to apologize perhaps. She hated that something both hopeful and anxious tightened in her stomach as she picked her phone up, swiped to unlock it.

Hated that feeling even more when she saw that it wasn't her mum, or Nate, who had sent her a message. It was Will. *Will.* Jesus, she'd all but forgotten him. Which said something, she supposed. **Hey, Evie. How's it going? Fancy meeting up for a drink?**

She stared at it, feeling… well, nothing. She nearly opened up Instagram, to check whether he was still with the perfect girlfriend. Then decided she just didn't *care*. And she certainly didn't want to see him. She should ring him maybe, shout at him, the way she should have when he'd first cheated on her. Should *rage* at him, for making her think that it was *her* fault, that there was something wrong with her. But it wouldn't make her feel better, and it wouldn't change what he did. So she put her phone down, screen facing the table.

She shouldn't have let Will get to her. Really he'd only been picking up on something she already thought about herself, and used it against her. And so, well... fuck him! *Yes, that's right, Scar – fuck him!* And she imagined Scarlett's laugh, that brilliant cackle. She could hear her voice, too. *Fuck 'em all!*

The door to the café opened and Evie glanced over, saw her mum. They looked nothing alike, as far as she could tell, though Scarlett had claimed they had a similar eye shape (eye *shape*, Scar? aren't everyone's eyes the same shape – sort of... eye-shaped?) and potentially similar eyebrows. But Ruth was short and slim, potentially always a little *too* thin, with darker skin than Evie's. Her hair was going grey, though she was clearly trying to cover it up with a dark brunette, and her face was softer, somehow, than Evie's. Evie and Scarlett used to speculate about what Evie's dad looked like – because surely that's who she resembled more – but Ruth had got rid of any photos, if she ever had any. Scarlett had once suggested doing a social-media search, but Evie had put her off the idea. Because what she'd said to Nate, climbing up that stupid cliff, was true: she'd never had any desire to know her dad. There was no point, was there, wanting someone who didn't want you? Something tightened at the base of her throat as Nate's face flashed into her mind, before she managed to squash it down.

'Hello, Evelyn!' Her mum bustled over, giving Evie a quick pat on the arm – her version of a hug – before settling down in the seat opposite her. 'You look well.'

Evie tried not to grit her teeth at that. She knew her mum didn't mean it, but it was so similar to what she'd said when Evie was first diagnosed with MS. *But you can't be ill, you look fine! Trust me, I know all about being ill. There was this one time…*

Ruth looked around the café. 'Do they do table service here?'

'No, you have to go up to the counter.'

'Oh.' She made a face. 'Eve, love, could you go up for me? I've had an awful journey, coming all the way from Cambridge, and my feet are ever so tired.'

'Sure. Okay.' She got to her feet, felt her muscles creak.

'Lovely.' Her mum beamed at her. 'I'll have an oat-milk latte – presumably they have oat milk here, it's that sort of place, isn't it? I'm going dairy-free. I think lactose is causing a recurring skin rash of mine.'

Evie got the coffee, came back and set it down in front of her mum.

'Oh, thank you. Actually, though, since you're up, I don't suppose you could grab me a sandwich or something? Something healthy? Like… hummus or something?'

Evie stared at her for a moment. 'Mum.'

'Hmm?'

'*You* could get your sandwich, you know.'

'Oh yes, but you're up, and like I said, I'm so tired. I think it's the menopause and—'

'Tired?' Evie felt her voice getting louder and she knew, on some level, that she might be being unreasonable here, but she couldn't seem to stop it. 'Tired? Mum, I am *always* tired. Do you get that?' People were looking over at her now, but she didn't care. *Fuck 'em. Fuck 'em all!* 'I have a *disease*, Mum. *I* am the one with the illness, not you.'

'But I—'

'My immune system is quite literally attacking my own body, and I can't do anything about that. I am on medication that I will probably have to be on for the rest of my life, and even that won't stop the disease progressing – though no one can tell me *how*, exactly, it will progress – because I didn't catch it earlier.' She sucked in a breath, closed her eyes. 'I didn't catch it early enough because I refused to go to the doctor when I first noticed symptoms. Because I was so determined not to jump at every little thing that was wrong with me.' She opened her eyes, saw Ruth looking at her a little warily – unused, perhaps, to this sort of outburst. 'Like you do, Mum.'

She came round the table and dropped down into the chair, her mum following her movements. Ruth cleared her throat. 'Well.'

Evie sighed. 'Well.'

'I know you have MS, Evelyn.' She took a sip of her coffee, winced slightly. 'Bit hot, isn't it? Anyway,' she continued, before Evie could say anything, 'I know you have an illness,' she repeated, 'but first, I didn't realize you blamed that on *me*—'

'I didn't say—'

'Yes, you did,' her mum said in a matter-of-fact tone. And Evie had, sort of, hadn't she? Because maybe she *did* blame her mum: not for the fact that she had it, because MS wasn't genetic, as far as they knew (or at least not wholly genetic), but for the fact that she hadn't caught it early enough for the DMTs – the treatment she had to be on indefinitely now – to be as successful as they could be. But, really, it wasn't her mum's fault, was it? Evie could have trusted herself more, about what she was feeling. She could have been less stubborn when Scarlett suggested she might as well *ask* the doctor. And the truth of it was that even if she had gone to the GP earlier, there was no guarantee they would have caught it right away. MS was one of the most difficult things to diagnose, she'd been told, over and over.

'And I'm sorry if me being ill a lot when you were growing up made you feel, for some bizarre reason, that you couldn't go to the doctor, but—'

'But you're *not* ill, Mum!' Evie said, throwing up her hands in exasperation. 'You *think* you are, but there's nothing wrong with you!'

'How do you know?' her mum asked, folding her hands, a little primly, in her lap. 'Are you a doctor?'

Evie frowned, but said nothing. Because whilst she truly believed that her mother's ailments were a figment of her imagination – something that seemed to be corroborated by multiple doctors over the years – hadn't she had similar conversations herself over the last few years? Hadn't she tried to explain to Henry, for instance, what she felt, even though he couldn't *see* anything wrong with her? Maybe it didn't even matter if it was in her mum's head. Because it still felt real to her, didn't it?

'And second,' her mum continued, 'I know you have MS, but you have never actually explained to me what that means.'

Evie's frown grew deeper. She was sure she had. Sure

she'd told her mum that she couldn't do certain things because she was… Had she, though? Had she actually gone further than that? Or had she simply expected her to know? 'I—'

'There is a lot of information out there.' Her mum picked up her coffee again. 'I should know: I check everything on Google. But there is hardly a straight answer on what MS is or, I suppose, how it affects people. So for all I know, you are genuinely feeling fine most of the time – and I'd hardly want to treat you as a sick person in that case, would I?'

Evie stared at her mum, dumbfounded. It was a level of insight she hadn't expected. 'Well, I… There's a few things.'

'And you'll tell me about them. But now, what time do you have to be back at work? Do we have time for that sandwich?'

Evie looked at her mum, the face that was both so familiar and yet strangely not, then got to her feet. 'We have time. I'll get us one each.'

'Oh, thanks, love. Hummus, yes? Or if not, then something with beans. They're supposed to be good for you, aren't they? Maybe you ought to try eating more beans, too.'

Chapter Thirty-Two

'Evie,' my mum says, enveloping her in a hug the moment she opens the door. 'We're so glad you came. Come in, come in.'

Evie steps over the threshold into my childhood home, and I see the way she braces for it, the onslaught of memories. Maybe, though, some of those memories will cause her to smile. Maybe they won't make her feel like she is drowning in grief. Because most of my memories of this house *are* happy, both with Evie and without. I remember falling down the stairs and crying, my mum sitting with me, talking about nonsense as she inspected my elbow, my head, until I wasn't crying but laughing. I remember Dad turning the music up so loud once, when I was a teenager and sulking in my room, that I came out shouting at him to turn it down because I was doing *homework*, which was a complete lie, and Dad just turning it up louder, until the three of us – me, him and Mum – all started dancing on the landing.

I remember Christmas Days, bounding into my parents' room to open stockings. One year Evie was there too. Why was that? I can't actually remember. I think maybe her mum had taken some work over Christmas, and my parents offered to have her – and they did a stocking for her and everything.

She's going to see her mum after this, Evie. I saw her text Ruth on the way. There's a relationship there that might actually be able to heal, in some capacity. Because her mum, despite everything, knew what Evie and I were to each other and tried to reach out. It's something I'd never have expected from Ruth, but I suppose I never really gave much thought as to what life would have been like for her, either. A young, single mother without a high-paying salary. I was always just thankful for my family, in comparison. I had that – had more than so many other people. More than Evie.

'Hello, Evie,' my dad says now, when Mum takes her into the kitchen. He envelops her in a slightly awkward hug. Why has Evie decided to come here today? Clearly it's been planned, but I missed the conversation, the moment of planning.

'Now you sit down, my love, I'll get you a glass of wine.' Mum bustles round the kitchen, pausing to lift the lid of a pan, checking whatever is inside it. I wish I could smell it – it's bound to be good. But I can only smell or taste or touch in the past, when I visit memories. Here and now, I am still forced to just *be.* Why? I wonder again. What's the point of all this? Surely it's leading to something; surely this can't be it, for ever?

She is making an effort, my mum, I can tell. Is it the first time they've seen Evie since my funeral? I think so, and that's probably why Mum's trying so hard to *bustle.* She puts a glass of white wine – light in colour, maybe a Pinot – down in front of Evie, then hands one to my dad.

He smiles at her, one that makes his eyes crease. She returns the smile before turning to pour herself a glass. It's a fleeting moment: barely noticeable. But I clock it. Something is different, between the night I saw my mum, crying on the bed, and now. Something has changed between them.

'Now, how are you, Evie?' Mum says, gesturing for her to sit at the kitchen table – the same round wooden one where I've had countless family dinners, where Evie and I, and various other friends at different points over my childhood, sat and ate fish fingers or jacket potatoes.

'I'm all right,' Evie says non-committally. But the thing is, this *all right* really does sound better than the *all right* she was handing out to people after I first died.

'Your symptoms, how are they?' Direct and to the point, my mum, as always.

A little shrug from Evie. 'Varies from day to day. It's okay at the moment.'

'Glad to hear it,' Dad pipes up, his voice a bit too booming, betraying his awkwardness. He was never as good at these things as Mum.

They settle into the conversation, starting with the small talk before things turn, inevitably, to me. They are smiling. There is the occasional blinking back of tears, of course, which I suppose is to be expected, but in general the three of them seem almost happy, sitting here, telling stories about me. My eighteenth birthday. The day Evie and I moved to London. Me crying on the first day of secondary school, and Evie having to coax me into going. I almost don't believe that; surely it would be the other way round?

Another example of how I've rewritten my memories over the years: me as the brave one, Evie the quieter one.

The day I first decided I wanted to be a fashion designer – Dad's the one who remembers that. Something I thought I'd forgotten, because what I wanted to do always seemed a part of me, without a clear beginning.

'We took her to this local village fair, you know the type. Outdoor furniture, lots of food, muddy-field car park, the lot. But there was this free activity for kids. What was she, Mel, about eleven?'

'About that,' Mum agrees. 'It was before secondary school, but she was old enough to be grumpy about being dragged along to the fete.'

'Anyway, she did this textiles thing – it was a free activity that you gave a donation to or whatever; all the kids have a go, you know the type.' I doubt Evie does, though, because when was the last time either of us went to a village fete? 'And Scarlett, she sat there for, I'm not kidding, a whole hour while we were freezing our arses off.' Mum smiles at the memory. 'She was determined to make something *beautiful* and kept correcting herself when she got it wrong. She was so damn proud of herself after that.' Dad shakes his head. 'And it stuck, I suppose.'

'I remember her telling me about it.' Evie smiles at them both. 'We talked about it so much: what our futures would be like.' It sits there for a moment – the fact that my future is no longer. 'There are a few people trying to pull together some of her last designs, actually,' Evie says a little awkwardly. 'They want to do a shoot and see if they can get her label off the ground, even though, you know…'

'Really?' Mum says with a beam. 'That's incredible. Who's doing that? I'd like to be in touch, thank them.'

'J— I mean, a few of her old colleagues,' Evie corrects herself, remembering that I never told them about Jason. I knew that it wasn't exactly the moral gold standard, having an affair with a married man.

'You'll put me in touch, will you?' Mum presses.

'Of course,' Evie says. 'I'll find out their details.' She doesn't have a choice, does she? And really, so what if Mum speaks to Jason? It doesn't mean she'll find out – and even if she does, I don't think it would be enough to change her memory of me.

'We'd love that, wouldn't we, Graham?'

Dad nods, clears his throat a little gruffly. He gives Mum a look, and Mum nods – it's clearly some kind of silent conversation because Dad disappears from the room, reappearing a few moments later with a big book. Like a guest book in a hotel or an old photo album: red, oddly sized, with a shiny laminated front.

'Thought you might like to see this,' Dad says and shoves the book a little unceremoniously into Evie's hands.

She opens it, flicks through, tracing certain pages with a finger. It's a bloody *scrapbook*, of all things. A scrapbook, not of childhood me, but of my career. Photos of my designs, cuttings of newspaper articles that either mention or allude to me in some capacity. Scraps of material from my final project at university – ones I thought I'd thrown out.

'I never showed her,' Dad says gruffly and Mum moves to him, gripping his shoulder in support. 'I don't know if she ever realized…'

'She knew,' Mum says softly – though it's a lie.

'And if she didn't know, then maybe she does now.' Evie, she was always the smartest one, wasn't she?

When it's time to go, Evie hugs them both, and Mum's eyes are shining when she pulls away. 'Now you stay in touch, won't you? Don't go disappearing on us.'

Evie nods. 'I promise.' And when she turns, waves goodbye, I see my dad put an arm around Mum, see her tuck her head onto his shoulder. I don't know how they've done it, but they are coming together again, my parents. Pulled together by grief, perhaps – rather than pulled apart, as Nate's parents were. So maybe they'll be okay. I don't doubt for a second that they'd rather have me back. That they would both, in an instant, choose me. But given that's not an option, it's nice, isn't it, that they have found their way back to each other? Another relationship healing, one I hadn't even realized had been breaking in the first place.

Evie starts the walk from my old house to hers. As she walks, she pulls out her phone, dials. I imagine it's the scrapbook – my *dad's* scrapbook – that's propelled her into action.

'Jason? It's Evie. I… You know you said you wanted something of Scarlett's? Well, I have something: a design for a dress. I can send a photo, if you like?'

'That's brilliant, Evie, but… I'm not sure it's in time now.'

'What?'

'When I didn't hear from you, I... Well, we're doing the shoot in a few days, and I doubt we'd have it ready by then. But send it over,' he adds quickly, clearly not wanting to hurt her feelings. 'We can try, for sure, if it fits and—'

'I have the dress,' Evie interrupts, a little bluntly.

'What?'

'I have the dress itself – I... Someone had it made. I don't know if that—'

'Can you send it to me?' Jason's excitement is almost palpable.

'I... Well, it's made for me.' Evie bites her lip. 'My size and everything, I mean. Scarlett designed it for me.'

'Okay,' Jason says and his voice has softened again. Say what you want about him, he was always good at reading people. 'How about you bring it on the day? I'll send you the details. We can see if it works, but maybe, if it's made for you, you should be there anyway.'

I see what he's doing, even if Evie doesn't. He might never have *met* Evie, but he heard about her plenty often enough. He knows what we meant to each other, and so he's offering to let her in, to be part of something that's for me.

I'm torn. I don't want to see the dress changed – it's Evie's dress. But I *do* want the label to happen. I want to live on, even after I fade.

Chapter Thirty-Three

Evie felt exhausted by the time she got home from work, the fatigue worse than it had been for a while, the kind that seeps into your bones and makes every effort feel heavy. So she was already not in the best of moods when she saw Nate, standing outside her block of flats. He'd been leaning against the brick building, scrolling through his phone, bare arms on show in the late-summer sun, but he straightened and slipped his phone into his pocket when he saw her.

She tried not to think of the last time she'd seen him, creeping around her bedroom in the dark. Tried to ignore the way her heart lurched – honestly, it actually *lurched* at the sight of him. 'What are you doing here?'

'You didn't answer my text.'

Well, it was accurate, she'd give him that. He'd texted her yesterday, finally. To ask how she was, ask if they could meet. But obviously she hadn't answered – it had taken Nate days to get in touch, and now he expected her to want to see him immediately? So that he could, what, try to let her down gently? No, thank you. She folded her arms, wishing she could just get inside, sink down on her sofa. He took a step towards her.

'Evie, we need to talk.'

'Why?'

'Because—'

'Because you feel guilty, after walking out on me?' No way was she making this easier on him. No way could he show up here, expecting her to be all bright and breezy. She would not let someone else treat her like she was nothing – not again.

'No. I mean, yes, I do, but—'

'Well, I'm over it,' she said shortly. 'So you can swan along. Don't worry about me.' She waved her hand to indicate the pavement, where he could keep walking.

Nate refused to move. 'I shouldn't have left like that.'

She sighed. 'Yes, well, it would have been nice if you'd waited until, say, nine a.m., for instance.'

'I should have come with you, to the appointment.'

His gaze was direct on hers, but Evie couldn't meet it and looked down to the tarmac instead. Because that was the real crux of the matter, wasn't it? Even if she hadn't technically asked him to come with her, it was what she'd meant, and they both knew it. And after everything – after telling her that he didn't see the illness when he saw her, after knowing how much losing Scarlett had cost her and opening up about his own brother – Nate had still chosen to walk away.

She pushed her hair out of her face. 'Look, it doesn't matter.' Not true, really. It *had* mattered. But she didn't want to have this conversation. Especially not on his terms. She wanted to go inside, shut the door and not speak to anyone for a good long while.

'It does,' Nate said firmly. 'It does. I freaked out, I'm sorry.'

'You freaked out,' Evie said flatly.

'Yes.'

'Right. Well, that makes it all better, thanks.'

'I didn't—'

'Let me guess,' Evie interrupted sharply, 'you didn't think it through?'

He winced. 'I don't... Not like that. I wanted to, obviously, I just didn't think of... later down the line.'

'Right,' Evie said again, making her tone as biting as she could, with this tiredness coursing through her very veins. 'So you were happy to sleep with me – multiple times, I might add – but were worried that I'd get a bit too clingy on day two, is that it? That I was coming to depend on you? Or maybe—'

'Look, honestly,' he interrupted, taking another step towards her. Evie eyed the pavement, checking there was a safe distance between them. 'It has nothing to do with you, it's—'

Evie scoffed. 'It's not you – it's me, right? Let me think, where have I heard that before?' She held a hand in the air, not caring that it was a touch dramatic. 'Wait a minute, it's coming to me...'

'I deliberately don't get involved with people, Evie.' Nate's voice was a soft rumble. 'It's why I travel about so much – well, not necessarily *why*, but it fits. The longest relationship I've had totals six months, and even that was arguably casual.'

'Fine,' she said, and now her voice was betraying her tiredness. 'You could have told me that at the time, instead of just leaving.'

'I know. I know…' He raked a hand over the back of his neck, the 'but' going unsaid. Someone in her block of flats – a man, who on earth *was* that? how did she not know who she lived with, for Christ's sake? – let himself in, eyeing Nate and Evie curiously.

'Look, Nate, what are you getting at here? Because I'm tired, so if you could get to the point, that would be really great.'

He swallowed, Adam's apple bobbing. Then he turned his gaze on her and she was hit with the full force of those liquid brown eyes. 'I do want it, Evie,' he said quietly. '*That* was the problem. That's why I freaked out. I want it; I want you.' She stared at him and her heart – her goddamn traitorous heart – jolted.

'You're just saying that.'

'I'm not.' He laughed, the sound a little self-scathing. 'I wanted you and it scared the shit out of me.'

Again that jolt, like something pumping through her. But she focused on the one word that made sense there. 'Wanted,' she said flatly. 'Past tense. And now you've taken the time to think, to come back to your senses, is that it?'

'No. No, of course not. I should have called earlier, I know that. I just wanted to be sure, so I didn't let you down later.'

'And, what: now you've made a decision and decided to clue me in?'

He grimaced. 'It's not like that.'

'What *is* it like then, Nate?'

'I… I don't know.'

'You don't *know*. Right. Well then, maybe you should make up your damn mind.' She started towards the entrance to the block of flats. He shifted to follow her. 'I don't need this,' she carried on. 'I've got my own problems to deal with.'

'I've been offered a job,' he blurted out. It made her stop, turn.

'What?'

'As a staff writer. For this business-to-business magazine in Australia.'

'Australia,' Evie repeated. She'd known he would probably leave, eventually, but… *Australia?*

'Work is getting a bit harder to come by and I need to take something and—'

'So Australia's the logical option? You didn't think of a job in London, for instance, where your whole family is?' *Where I am.* She didn't say it out loud. Instead she clung to her resolve. She didn't need this – didn't need another guy making her feel like shit.

'I haven't said yes.'

'What?' God, she was articulate today.

'I haven't said yes, because of you.'

'Because of me.' *Can you do more than bloody echo, Evie!*

'Because I wanted to see how you felt about it.'

'About you moving to Australia.'

'Yes.' He moved, a little tentatively, towards her. Towards where she was standing next to the door, keys in hand.

'Would you… would you want me to stay? If it were an option?'

She scowled. 'I hate "ifs". *Is* it an option? Do *you* want to stay?' Did she even want him to? Her heartbeat grew faster, more frantic in its pounding – at the thought that she had to say the right thing, make the right decision, without properly thinking it through.

Nate reached out, put a hand on the side of her neck. He'd got so close to her without her noticing. And he'd left her, and now here he was back again, trying to put her in some sort of…

'You can't just decide it's fine now,' she snapped. 'You can't just decide you want… something… now. It can't all be on your terms.'

He smiled wryly. 'Trust me, it's not.'

And she got it, because she thought she was starting to get *him*. Nate wanted *her* to ask him to stay. He didn't want to make the decision, either – because staying, it would scare him too, wouldn't it? It would be a break from his lifestyle and, despite his talk of lack of fear, she felt sure *that* was what would scare him. So instead of making the decision himself, he'd snuck out. Yes, he'd come back, but only to put the decision on her. And she couldn't bear it. Because what if she said yes, what if she asked him to stay and then he left anyway? Exactly like Will had. Exactly like *Scarlett* had. Even Scarlett, the one person she'd thought would never leave her, had been planning to, in the end.

So she closed her eyes. 'I think you should go,' she whispered.

'What?'

'To Australia.' And she would hold herself together. She'd dealt with worse than this. She didn't need him, didn't need— It hit her then, hot and sharp, a band crushing her ribcage. She doubled over, wincing, as the electric pain shot through her.

'Evie? Shit, Evie? What's wrong?'

'It's okay,' she gasped. 'It will pass.' The 'MS hug', her doctor had called it. And – for her – a sure sign that a relapse was on its way.

'Let's get you upstairs. Do you have paracetamol? I think I do, in the car. Hang on.'

'No,' Evie said on a laboured breath. 'Drugs don't help. Not those kinds of drugs.' This kind of pain – the MS kind – didn't respond to pain medication, as she'd learned the hard way. She stood back up to full height gingerly as the feeling started to subside. 'This is what I mean, Nate,' she whispered and was alarmed to find that her eyes were stinging, her vision blurring. She blinked furiously. She would *not* cry. Not in front of him. 'I'm not well. I'm never going to be – not completely. I'm barely getting by myself, and then *you* come into my life, and you…' She shook her head. 'I can't go there. I need to sort myself out first. And you, it sounds like you don't even know what you want. Not really.'

'I do, I—'

But she laughed, a sad pathetic sound. 'You just told me you didn't. Because if you were sure, if you were really sure, then you wouldn't be asking me, would you? You'd have already decided to stay.'

He stared at her and because of the look in his eye, because he looked so... *broken* in that moment, she took his hand, squeezed.

'It won't work, Nate. Even if you were one hundred per cent sure, it wouldn't work. All those adventures you want to go on? I'm not going to be able to keep up with you.' She blinked back tears, told herself to stop it. Told herself she was doing the right thing – for them both.

'I told you,' he said gruffly. 'I don't care about any of that. I don't care about the MS.'

'Well, maybe you should,' she said on a sigh. 'It's unpredictable.'

'I'm unpredictable.'

'It's only going to get worse.'

'*I'm* only going to get worse.' He tried for a smile, which she didn't return. 'Evie...' His voice was pleading, and she closed her eyes against it.

'Go,' she whispered. 'Please just go.'

And the worst thing about it was that he did exactly that. She didn't want him to; she wanted him to know, somehow, what the right thing to do was, even though *she* didn't know it herself. Wanted him to take her in his arms, hug her, tell her it would all be okay. Tell her that this time he was staying, no matter how hard she pushed him away. But instead he turned and left her there. Standing alone – like she'd wanted.

Chapter Thirty-Four

Evie is sitting in the dark – blinds down, lights off – when there is a knock at her door. She's been like this for a whole day, as far as I can gather. There is no sign of her having gone to work; she's in her pyjamas, sitting on the sofa.

'Who is it?' she calls, making no effort to get up. Her voice is a little slurred, a sure sign that a relapse has her in its grip.

'Astrid!'

Evie is stiff as she gets up, crosses to the front door. Everything looks painful, forced – this is how she was a few days before our argument. Is this what she's going to do, every time a relapse takes hold? Retreat from the world? Can I judge her for that, when I have no clue how it feels?

'Are you ready?' Astrid asks when Evie opens the door. 'You don't look ready. I told you to wear something nice.' Astrid is all in black: black polo-neck jumper, skinny black jeans. Hair short again – maybe her mum helped her cut it this time. She looks older like this, rather than in her baggy hoodies or school uniform.

'I…' Evie's fingers flex on the doorway. 'Astrid, I'm so sorry, I don't think I can come.'

Astrid just stares at her and it's weird, considering that I've never actually spoken to this girl, considering that she is a teenager – and one vastly different from the type of teenager I was – but I feel a sort of kinship with her in that moment. Because I *know* that look. I must have worn it myself countless times over the last few years of my life. The disappointment in my friend. Unlike me, though, Astrid doesn't bother to mince her words, perhaps because she doesn't fully get it. Did *I* fully get it?

'What?' Astrid asks. 'Why?'

'I—'

'You *promised*. You have to be there, I *need* you there. The music teacher is rubbish! I need *you* to warm me up. I need...' She's gulping in breaths now, shades of panic showing in her eyes. 'We worked on this together – it won't work if you're not there.'

'It will,' Evie says, pulling her cardigan, that fucking holey cardigan, closer to her. 'Honestly, Astrid, you'll be great and—'

'Why?' Astrid interrupts, still staring at Evie in that imploring way. 'What is so important that you can't come? You *said* you'd be there; you said you'd put it in your calendar.'

Evie said she'd meet Jason today, too – does she remember that? When he sent her the details, it turned out that he was arranging the shoot for the same day as Astrid's school concert, and he said he'd push it back a few hours so that she could make it. And now, what: she's bailing on that too? I think of my dress, in Evie's wardrobe – will it ever see the outside world, ever have a moment to shine? Not just because of the shoot – I surprise myself to find that I don't really care about that – but because of Evie. Will she ever wear it in public, brilliant and daring, like I wanted her to? She doesn't *like* going out in public during a relapse; that's what she's told me, countless times. But if she never knows when a relapse is due, how is she supposed to plan her life around it? What if it hits her on, say, her wedding day? I know that's the problem – that's the part she hates.

'It's because of that guy, isn't it?' Astrid is saying now, her words accusing.

'Which guy?'

Oh, *come on*, Evie. As *if* she's playing dumb here.

'The journalist guy,' Astrid says impatiently. 'Nate Ritchie.' So she's somehow figured out his surname then, showing off her detective skills. Does Evie notice how her face tightens at the mention of his name? Does her heart catapult at the sound of it, the way mine used to when someone mentioned Jason's name at work? I try it out again now. Jason. Jason. Is it just because I no longer have a beating heart that I don't feel that familiar lurch, or is it something else?

'No, it's not him, it's—'

'It is,' Astrid insists. 'I heard you arguing, downstairs.'

Evie raises her eyebrows, clearly trying to change the tone. 'Did you now?'

Astrid turns pink, but keeps her glare on Evie's face, arms folded.

She hasn't called Nate since he showed up, three days ago now – and he hasn't called her, either. Maybe because she shut him down, when he was clearly so desperate for her to throw him a line. Both of them unable to do anything without the reassurance of one another – so different, yet annoyingly similar in this one way. I want her to call him and have tried sending general urgings, thinking it *really* hard, to try and influence her in some way. She could even message him: a quick text surely. I wonder when it shifted – when did I decide to side with Nate? When did I start rooting for him?

'It's not that,' Evie says on a sigh. 'Honestly. It's… my MS, it's bad today.'

'Bad?' Astrid gives her a sceptical look. 'Bad how?'

'It's difficult to explain.'

'Do you need to go to the hospital?'

'No, it's not that bad.'

'Can you still sit, get in a taxi?'

Evie hesitates. 'Well, technically, I suppose so.'

'Well then.' Astrid folds her arms. 'I don't see why you can't come.'

I see it more than Astrid, I think. The tiredness is getting to Evie, she's stiff and in pain. But she's also not left the house all day. She's been sitting on the sofa in the dark.

She shakes her head – a sad movement. 'I'm so sorry, Astrid.'

'Fine.' She lifts her chin in the air. 'I'll do it without you.' With that, Astrid turns on her heel and storms back to her side of the corridor, while Evie shuts the door, rests her head against it. If I was there – really *there*, I mean – I'd tell her to go. I'd *make* her go. Then again, maybe I wouldn't have any luck, either. Because when it's a bad day, I've learned, nothing can make Evie leave.

Nothing.

Though that's not entirely true, is it?

Just like that, I'm at a round table in a big event space, in a hotel in central London – one of the mid-range ones, not like the Ritz, but still posh. There are people all around, all of us seated at circular tables with white linen, like at a wedding, and there are half-full wine glasses smudged with fingerprints, napkins dumped on the tables, upturned bottles of wine in the cooler, as people look around hopefully for one another. Coffee and tea are starting to be brought out, and there's a space of wooden floor at the front where someone is fiddling with the microphone. I am looking around and I know who I'm looking for: Jason is supposed to be here. It's after the 'I love you' moment and although nothing has been resolved, although he hasn't yet said he'll leave his wife, he promised he'd be here tonight. But he's nowhere to be seen and there's an empty space on the seat that should be his.

The man with the microphone at the front starts to speak, and Evie prods my arm.

I don't even have to look at her to know she's having a bad day. I remember the wincing, the way the tremor had been getting worse, that I had to open the taxi door for her. She looks tired, despite the make-up, and her whole body seems stiff.

But she is here. For me.

Because this is an awards dinner. It's not anything big, only a company-wide thing, but it is still special. I remember that it is actually really boring – Evie and I will at one point entertain ourselves by playing a game of noughts and crosses on my napkin. But the point is, I win: the debut fashionista award.

I didn't appreciate it at the time. I assumed there would be bigger and better things to come – that soon I'd be at the *real* awards. I never lost that conviction that I would make it. I always thought of it as a good thing, but maybe it stopped me realizing what I already had.

And as I look around again for Jason, I realize I didn't really appreciate that Evie had come out that night. That she made herself do it for me – maybe because she doubted that Jason would show, which she was right about. Because she knew, even if I didn't, that I needed her there.

Chapter Thirty-Five

Julie ran towards Evie the moment she stepped into the school hall. 'Brilliant! I'll take you backstage, Anna's told the teachers to expect you.'

Evie frowned as Julie ushered her down the side of one line of plastic-backed chairs. 'Why? I told her I wasn't coming.'

'Something you ought to know about my daughter – she tends to know things before we do.'

Evie didn't get a chance to respond to that because she had to climb, stiffly, up the small flight of stairs that led to a stage and then through some curtains to the 'backstage' area, which was basically a bunch of kids jostling for space and a whole lot of music.

'We only have five minutes!' yelled a woman with a loud, booming voice and a clipboard.

'Yay, you made it just in time.' Astrid's voice arrived before she did.

'Astrid, I'm so sorry—'

Astrid held up a hand. 'We don't have time for that. I'm stuck on the last arpeggio, can we check it quickly?'

'Look, I just want to say—'

Astrid rolled her eyes in a way that made Evie stop. 'I get it: you're sorry, blah-blah. I knew you wouldn't *actually* bail.'

Evie gave an uncertain laugh and glanced at Julie, who winked and said, 'I'll leave you to it.'

They went through the trickier bits of the piece, with Evie making encouraging noises all the time. There was no point correcting anything at this stage – she knew that first hand. Either you had it or you didn't, and pointing out mistakes would only make Astrid more nervous.

'And that's it!' The booming voice sounded. 'Places, people.'

Evie squeezed Astrid's shoulder as another girl, around the same age as Astrid, came over – long, wiry hair, wearing a black dress with black tights. She glanced at Evie, then looked down at the ground, perhaps a little shyly. 'I, um, just wanted to say good luck.'

'You too,' Astrid replied. 'Not that you need it,' she added quickly. 'You'll be great.'

The girl nodded, then scuttled away. Evie tried to keep a straight face as she asked casually, 'Who's that? Cello girl?'

Astrid blushed in a way that highlighted the vulnerability that so clearly lurked beneath the surface. 'Her name is Lily.'

'Lily, huh?'

Around them, everyone was moving towards the black curtain. The woman with the posh, loud voice looked over at Evie accusingly.

'I have to go,' Evie said. 'You'll be great, okay?'

'What if I'm not?' Astrid asked as Evie stepped away.

'If you're not, then all it means is that next time will be better.'

'That's not overly inspiring, you know.'

'Sorry. How about: if you're not, then…'

'Paula?' The booming woman was flapping her clipboard as she looked around. 'Paula! No, sorry, I mean Mrs Gregory! You're supposed to be doing the introduction!'

Evie took Astrid's hands in hers. 'It doesn't matter if you're not great. You do it because you love it, remember? And that means, no matter what happens – even if you mess it up entirely – other people will feel that love too.'

She squeezed Astrid's hands one more time, then turned to leave, shuffling towards the exit to the back-stage area.

'Evie?' Astrid called and she turned. '*That's* more inspiring.' And Evie grinned.

When she made it down the stairs and back into the main school hall, Julie was waiting for her. 'She okay?' Julie asked. Evie nodded, and Julie smiled. 'You look lovely, by the way.'

'Thanks,' Evie said, resisting the temptation to smooth down the dress self-consciously. She was wearing Scarlett's dress. It had felt right, even if she was overdressed for a school concert, because it came back to what the two of them loved: music and fashion. And Evie reckoned that Scarlett would have been pleased she was wearing it.

'I've got us three seats,' Julie said, leading Evie through the rows of chairs.

'Why three – does she come down when she's done?'

'No, the third seat's not for her. He arrived before you did. Astrid told him where to sit.'

And then she saw him. Nate. Sitting in the middle of a bloody school hall.

Evie stumbled to a stop and stared at him. 'What on earth are you doing here?' she asked, as Julie took a seat and made a show of looking through the programme.

Nate raised his hands in a helpless gesture. 'I was given instructions to be here. You didn't know I was coming?'

'No. I didn't even know *I* was coming.'

'*Parent Trap* again?'

Evie pulled her hand through her hair. 'A really bloody weird *Parent Trap*. How did she even get the ticket to you?'

Nate shrugged. 'Came through the letter box at Noah's yesterday, so apparently she discovered where I live.'

Evie found she wasn't surprised by that.

'Do you want me to leave?' Nate asked quietly, his gaze still on hers – waiting, assessing.

Evie looked at him, allowed something to settle. 'No,' she said on an outward breath. 'Stay.'

The smile that lit his face as she sat down was instantaneous. And maybe it was a good thing that the lights dimmed then.

'Showtime,' she murmured.

It was a big ensemble piece to start with and Evie felt nerves flutter in her stomach, like it was *her* up there. And when it was time for Astrid's solo, with the spotlight on her, Evie felt tears spark in her eyes.

'She's brilliant,' Julie murmured, and Evie could only nod. She didn't even know *why* she felt so goddamn emotional.

Nate took her hand and Evie gripped it back. It turned out Astrid was right: Evie *was* still a part of something. Even though it wasn't her up there performing, this was proof that music could still have a role in her life. And performing – well, that wasn't the bit she'd loved anyway.

At the interval, when Nate excused himself to go to the loo, Evie followed Julie out of the hallway into the school canteen, which, despite the fact that none of the ovens were on, somehow still smelled a little of grease.

'Cup of tea?' Julie asked and Evie nodded, started to go with her, only for Julie to flap a hand at her. 'Stay.' She pointed at one of the canteen tables. 'Sit.' Hardly in a position to argue, Evie did exactly that, feeling both physically and emotionally exhausted.

She had barely two seconds to herself before the woman with the booming voice descended on her. 'You're Anna's tutor, aren't you? Anna James?'

'Er, I wouldn't say tutor exactly, but I—'

'You've done wonders. Wonders!' Was this the music teacher Astrid was on about? The one whom Astrid had deemed useless? 'She was all shaky and nervous when she arrived – talented, but you've fine-tuned her indeed.'

'Well,' Evie said, feeling slightly affronted on Astrid's behalf, 'I think she did most of that herself.'

But booming woman wasn't listening, looking instead over her shoulder, back at the canteen entrance. 'What's that, Derek? Yes, yes, it's the recorders next! Don't ask me, it was Paula's idea.' She turned back to Evie. 'Anyway, do you have a card? Some of the parents are always asking for a private music tutor and I simply don't have the time. And is it only the violin you teach or everything?'

'I—'

'You'll email me, yes? I've got to get back. Anna's mum has my details.'

She watched the woman barrel away, feeling dumbfounded. A tutor. She *wasn't* a tutor, but she could imagine it. She doubted it would be enough to make a living from – in London at least – but the idea certainly felt far from horrible.

Still waiting for Julie, she slipped her phone out of her handbag. There was a voicemail waiting for her, from a number she didn't recognize. Jason? She was supposed to be there in an hour. With a slight roll in her stomach, she dialled her voicemail and heard a brisk female voice.

'Hello, Ms Jenkins, this is Kate from Garrett Whitelock Letting Agents. I'm calling because we had you and a Scarlett Henderson down to rent out a flat at Borough Market in May, but from what I can see in our records, it fell through. I can't reach Scarlett, but you were the secondary contact we have listed, and we were wondering if one or both of you might be interested in a new property we have available? It's a similar location, *so* convenient for public-transport links, newly fitted kitchen to *die* for…'

Evie didn't listen to the rest of the message. She felt suddenly lightheaded. Scarlett hadn't been planning on leaving her. She'd been planning on taking Evie with her.

She hadn't realized how much it had been weighing on her, despite her determination to push it aside. She only fully realized now, as the weight disappeared. She looked around, feeling the need to tell someone, to laugh, to stand up and *announce* it. But everyone was still milling around – nothing had changed. She supposed it didn't alter anything, not really. Yet it did. It *did*.

She saw that Nate had come out of the bathroom and was now standing with Julie. He already had her laughing, the total charmer. It made her smile a little. As if he could sense her gaze, he looked back over to her, then said something to Julie and crossed to Evie.

'You okay?' he asked.

'Yeah, I'm okay…' She laughed, stood up, nearly lost her balance, then laughed again.

Nate reached out a hand to steady her. 'Was the tea spiked?'

'No. Well, I haven't had one yet, so maybe. I mean, how well do we really *know* Julie?'

They both looked over to her, with Nate playing along.

'No, it's Scarlett, she…' But Evie couldn't really explain, because she had never told him about the letter in the first place. 'It doesn't matter. Look,' she said decisively, 'there's somewhere I need to go, after this.'

'Oh?'

Out of the corner of her eye, Evie saw Astrid talking to Lily. The girls had their heads bowed together, and Astrid said something to make Lily laugh. Something tugged at Evie's heart and she smiled up at Nate. So what if it made her vulnerable? 'I was wondering: would you come with me?' This time she left no doubt that it was a question.

And this time he answered immediately. 'Of course.' Just like that. 'And by the way,' he added with a smile, 'you look beautiful tonight. I should have told you that sooner.'

Evie swept her hands down her body to demonstrate the dress. 'What, this? It's just something I had lying around…'

He grinned. 'Well, it looks like it was made for you.'

Scarlett's name was there, unsaid, but hovering between them. But for the first time it wasn't in a sad way. It was just *there*, and suddenly Evie thought she understood what Nate's mum had been talking about. That she might be able to see a way, in the future, to take Scarlett's brightness and keep it with her.

Chapter Thirty-Six

I watch Jason descend upon Evie the moment she arrives at the little studio in Soho. 'Thank you so much for coming,' he says, his voice warm. 'Everyone? This is Evie.' But 'everyone' does not seem to care who Evie is. I'm used to the general chaos before a shoot, but I can tell Evie is feeling overwhelmed.

Jason looks curiously at Nate, but shakes his hand politely when Nate introduces himself simply as Evie's friend. I have a moment remembering Nate on his bike, careering around the corner, hearing that carefree, infectious laugh. I can feel my body, stepping off the pavement. I resist going back there, though. It's coming, I've accepted that now. I know I can't keep putting it off. But right now I'm enjoying marvelling at the turn of events – that the man I stopped to help is now here, with Evie, at a shoot for *my* label.

Jason does a quick assessment of Evie, eyes travelling up and down her body, and then lets out a little sigh. 'This is it, isn't it? This is the dress.'

'Sorry,' Evie says quickly. 'I'm only realizing now that I probably shouldn't have actually *worn* it here, should I? But if you have anything I can change into or…' She glances at Nate, who gives her a crooked grin.

'Hey, I'm all up for you walking home naked.'

310

She gives him a light hit on the arm, though I see her face soften – not quite a smile, she's too nervous for that, but almost. She's given in so quickly, really, to that easy way of his – I think I was right in my split-second assessment of him. He *is* infectious. And it's good for her, isn't it?

'No, no,' Jason says and then he walks round her. He claps his hands decisively. 'You should do it.' He elaborates without being asked. 'You should be in the shoot. This dress, it's perfect on you. It'll be too big for our model, but it's amazing on you.'

And it *is* amazing, if I say so myself. It tucks in at all the right places, and the way it moves when Evie walks makes her look graceful, even though she's arguably not. The colour is striking, there's no other word for it. Honestly, I'm glad she wore it to the concert, but *this* is what she should have been wearing at the Ritz. I have a fleeting moment when I imagine giving the dress to her myself for her thirtieth birthday in August. Making her wear it as we went out for drinks, getting dressed up myself. I'll never do that again, will I? Never have one of those nights when you get dressed up for the hell of it. It gives me a pang, but maybe not as acute as it once was. What will Evie do, on her thirtieth? Will I still be around to see it? Perhaps she'll still wear the dress.

'What do you think, D?' Jason calls over to one of the stylists he works with – only ever known as 'D'. I swear I don't actually know her full name.

'Oh, totally,' D says. 'It'll be so authentic.'

'Authentic,' Jason says with a nod. 'Exactly right.'

311

Jesus, we are a bunch of twats when we all get together, aren't we? *Authentic* – really.

Evie is sort of shoehorned into hair and make-up, without actually agreeing to anything. Nate talks to her the whole time, and I really thank God for him, because I reckon there's a strong chance she would bail without him.

Though maybe I should give her more credit than that; maybe that's always been the problem. It's why I didn't tell Evie about the flat – and thank fuck she found out about it. I swear I am sending *all* the good vibes to Kate Whatshername right now.

Of course Evie jumped to the wrong conclusion when she opened the letter. I would have done, too. I know – I should have told her. I was going behind her back, trying to move her out. But I'd assumed she'd say no. And here is Nate, always encouraging her to say yes to things, whereas I'd been taking it for granted that she'd say no. When? I can't pinpoint, exactly, when I started treating Evie like that: a fragile thing, who shouldn't be allowed to make her own decisions. I suppose it was gradual – as her illness progressed.

But the new flat, I was doing it for us both, honestly I was. I was fed up of our Clapham flat, obviously, but I also thought it would be nicer for Evie, if she was insisting on staying home all the time. But maybe that was the wrong way to think about it – because maybe it would have been moving her to a bigger prison, allowing her to stagnate, and maybe she wouldn't have done all the things she's done since I died.

'You ready, Evie?' Jason asks, full of professionalism, totally in his element here. There's no doubt about it: he's still sexy. He's also still wearing his wedding ring.

I feel a rush of certainty then. He was never going to leave his wife for me. Maybe he shouldn't have done. I wanted it – and it felt more real than anything that had come before, a stream of guys I'd dismissed. But maybe it's a sliding scale; maybe the excitement I'd felt wasn't because he was The One, like I thought, but because of something else: chemistry, me being the right age, him being unavailable, whatever. I've never really been into over-analysing and all that psychoanalysis bullshit, but, like I said, I'm having a moment of clarity right now. And seeing Nate with Evie, what I had with Jason does not compare.

When they are done with Evie, she has a proper *She's All That* moment. She even *stumbles*, like Laney does when she falls down the stairs.

She is, objectively, not a very good model, but that's not the point. She is there and she is doing it. Jason is talking to Evie, soothing; he always was good at soothing the models. But although I'm aware of him, although I'm right there with him and there is no wife around, no other people – although I *could* look at him if I wanted to – it's Evie I can't stop watching. It is Evie, not Jason, who I want to be with in that moment.

Chapter Thirty-Seven

'Did that actually just happen?' Evie was standing outside on a street in Soho, still wearing the dress, her face caked with make-up, her hair done up. The daylight had faded now, with that artificial glow of London settling in its place.

'I can confirm it did,' Nate said, taking her hand and squeezing. 'You were brilliant.'

'Hardly. But I did it.' And she'd done it for Scarlett. At one point Jason had looked at her under the lights, and she'd known that was why he was doing it too. She still didn't think Scar had made the best choice there, but maybe it wasn't easy to control who you fell in love with. After all, here she was, standing next to the man who— No. She was not thinking about that. She was not thinking about *either* of those things.

Nate turned her to face him, put his hands on her waist, where the dress tucked in. She reached up, wrapped her arms around his neck. Why did this always feel easy with him? Like she was meant to be here, standing out in the glow of Soho with him.

'Thank you,' she said. 'For coming with me.'

He squeezed her waist. 'Evie…'

'Uh-oh. That doesn't sound like a good "Evie".'

He stepped away from her, ran a hand over his jawline. 'I said yes.'

'You said yes,' she repeated. But she didn't need him to explain. She already knew, from the widening pit in her stomach. 'To the job in Australia,' she finished.

He nodded. She was aware of the way he was watching her, maybe expecting her to snap at him. But she couldn't, could she? Because she'd *told* him to take it.

'When do you leave?'

'Tomorrow.'

'*Tomorrow?* Jesus, you don't do things half-arsed, do you?' But she knew that, didn't she?

'I've already stayed here way longer than I meant to. I was supposed to be here for Noah's birthday, that was it. But then...'

She swallowed a lump in her throat. 'Okay. So this is goodbye?' She was trying to make her voice calm, efficient. But it was too quiet. It felt too difficult to get it out.

'No. I mean, yes, for now, but... We can stay in touch, right? And I'll be back in London at some point, I'm sure.'

'Yes,' she said automatically. 'Yes, of course, we'll stay in touch.' But she didn't believe it. He'd be off, living out his adventure, and she'd be... Where would she be? Not in London. Stupid that it'd taken her so long to realize it. But she didn't want to be in London – and there was nothing keeping her here, was there?

'Evie,' Nate was saying, 'I'm sorry, I...'

But she took his hand. 'Don't be. You have to do what's right for you.' Something in his expression twisted at that, but he said nothing. 'And, Nate, whatever happens now, I want to tell you…' she moved her hand to his cheek, rested it there, 'I'm glad I met you.' And it was true. It didn't stop her wishing that he hadn't been there that day. That Scarlett was still here, lighting up the world around her. But she couldn't help but be glad she'd met Nate, in spite of that. And they were two feelings that were going to have to live side-by-side, next to one another.

He reached his own hand up, placed it over hers. 'And I'm glad I met you, Evie Jenkins.'

They stood like that for a little while longer, and though they made no further move towards one another, Evie felt more connected to him than she ever had – more connected, maybe, than she'd ever been to another person, like her very heart had settled, matching itself to his. So maybe it didn't matter that he was leaving, that she might never see him again. Because, like Scarlett, the time with Nate had changed her. And that was something that would never leave her, no matter what.

Chapter Thirty-Eight

Nate is a real idiot, isn't he? Right now, he is packing. He is actually *packing*, and it turns out his stuff all depressingly fits into one suitcase. My disappointment in him is almost tangible, so much so that I'm surprised it's not manifesting itself somehow. It's not that I think Evie won't survive him leaving – not any more. I saw the resolution in her last night. Exhausted, fed up, upset. She was all of those things. But there was a steeliness there, the bit that would come out whenever she would make herself perform. It's been a while since I've seen that – even before Will cheated on her. But now that it is back, I don't think it's going away so easily.

So no, it's not that I'm worried this will send Evie over the edge – I think she'll get through it, even if she's *also* an idiot, because, really, she could have protested a bit more. It's just that I thought Nate would fight for her. Because they are good for each other: it's clear he could use a bit more stability in his life, and she could certainly use a bit more excitement.

He finishes packing, does a quick, cursory glance around the room at Noah's house – perfectly spare room-like with the blue walls and an inoffensive painting of the sea – then lugs his suitcase out of the room and down the stairs. His mum and brother are both sitting at the kitchen table when he gets there.

Noah stands up, claps him on the back. 'What time's your taxi?'

'Ten minutes.'

'Time for a quick send-off then?' Noah gets down a bottle of brandy – *brandy*, really? 'Don't tell Camille,' he adds, pouring out three glasses.

Nate sinks into one of the chairs. For a guy about to jet off to Australia, he doesn't exactly look happy.

'So you're really doing this then?' his mum asks.

Nate accepts the glass of brandy that his brother offers him. 'Looks like it.'

Noah and his mum exchange a look over his head that I don't think he sees. 'You could still change your mind,' Noah says, his voice *ever* so casual.

'What would be the point of that?' Nate mutters, taking a sip of his brandy. Then he frowns up at Noah. 'You and Camille, you happy?'

Noah raises his eyebrows. 'It's taken you this long to ask?'

'Well, it's not usually the type of thing you ask, is it? It's sort of… assumed. But are you?'

'Yeah,' Noah says with a shrug. 'We're happy.'

Is it that easy? Noah makes it *sound* easy, but I doubt it's all plain sailing – I'm learning now that it never is.

'You got married too young, if you ask me,' Grace says grandly. 'Not that you did.'

Noah rolls his eyes. 'Thanks for that input – really useful, two kids and a mortgage later.'

Grace holds up a finger. 'Let me finish.' She looks between the two of them – her two remaining sons. 'I know we don't really talk about this, but I know it hit you both hard when Nick died.' Nate grimaces, and Noah drops eye contact. '*You*,' she said, gesturing at Noah, 'decided to get all grown-up so quickly, settled down before you'd even given yourself the chance to process.' Her face softens. 'But that worked out well for you, so I'm hardly one to judge.'

'Hardly,' Noah mutters, then he and Nate exchange a small smile.

'And *you*,' she turns on Nate, 'I know that you're worried, my darling, about ending up like Nick. Don't interrupt,' she says when Nate opens his mouth, and Nate makes a face, but doesn't speak. 'But you're not like Nick. Not in the way that worries you.'

'How do you know?' Nate asks quietly.

'Because I know *you*. But I do worry that if you keep moving around, you'll end up without the support that you might find you need.'

'Depression hates a moving target,' Nate mutters, twirling his glass of brandy on the table. Noah frowns at him, and Nate waves a hand in the air. 'It's one of the things I found, when I looked up...'

'Suicide,' Grace says. 'No point not saying the word – it won't make it any less true, or any less awful.'

'Right, well.' Nate clears his throat. 'Anyway, the point is that if you keep moving, keep *doing*, then you're less likely to get hit by depression.'

Is he seriously worried about that? Does he think he might get hit with that kind of illness? I suppose there's no way of knowing, is there? Not without living in someone else's skin. He *seems* so happy, generally, but then you know what they say about comedians – they're the most depressed of the lot. I try to imagine what it must be like, living with that. Knowing that someone in your family got so down that they literally couldn't stand living any more.

Grace stands up, crosses to Nate and places a hand on his cheek – pure motherly affection. 'I think you need to ask yourself: are you moving around so much because you want to or because you're worried about what might happen if you sit still? Because they are two very different things.' She pats his cheek, picks up her glass and holds it out to Noah for a refill.

'Were *you* happy? You and Dad?' It's Noah who asks, but Nate sits up straighter. I wonder how long this conversation has been coming – a while, maybe.

Grace takes a slow sip of brandy. 'Nick broke us,' she says. 'No point in denying that. But...' She smiles, like she's looking into the past. 'We were happy, yes, before that. Maybe "meant to be" isn't really a thing, but I still believe that we were meant to be in each other's lives. We gave one another love and happiness for as long as we were both able, and I'll take that.'

Nate frowns. 'Even though...'

'Even though nothing,' Grace says. 'There's no point in the "what ifs". Not when we're talking about the past.'

She throws back her brandy, sets the empty glass down on the table. Then she levels a look at Nate. 'What ifs for the future, though, now that's another question entirely.'

Nate's phone lights up and he looks at it in a resigned sort of way. 'Taxi's here.'

He stands up and Grace envelops him in a huge hug. 'You'll be okay,' she says firmly.

Noah claps him on the back, gives him a one-armed hug, and Nate grabs the handle of his suitcase. 'You'll be back for Christmas, won't you?'

'I'll try.'

'I've already promised the girls, so you'll have to do better than try,' he says with a wink.

Nate doesn't look back as he hands his suitcase over to the driver to haul into the boot, then buckles up.

'Any preference on radio station?' the driver asks. 'Classic, Heart, Radio One…'

'Anything,' Nate says, looking out of the window as his brother's perfect house pulls away. 'Whatever. Classic's fine.'

Violins, I plead silently. *Come on, violins.*

And it is! It is a piece of music with bloody *violins* playing! And I know it might not have been my powers-from-the-beyond that made it happen, but do you know, I will fucking take it – because it does what I thought it would do. It makes Nate stiffen. Makes him shake his head, pulling a hand through his hair. And then it makes him smile, just a little.

I know, then. This is *his* moment. Whether or not he

321

realizes it too right now is a different matter. But sooner or later, he's going to look back at this moment and he's going to figure it out. I know he is.

Chapter Thirty-Nine

I'm pulled to Evie, almost without conscious thought. I want to tell her, *It's okay, he'll come back for you!* Instead I watch as she sits by the window, looking out at the street below – the window where Astrid stands to play, while they practise. Evie's moving out of the flat next week and she cancelled those viewings she had planned. So it looks like she really *is* moving out of London. She's going to stay with her mum for a few weeks, while she figures out what to do next.

And – wait for it – she quit her job. She actually told that prick he could find someone else to book his daughter's birthday bouncy castle. She's not even working the full notice, because Henry told her she didn't need to. All of this *today*, I might add. Big day for Evie. I like to think I had a part in it, because it was after my photoshoot – well, mine in name – that she came to this realization. I wonder how long it would have taken her otherwise.

She's started to pack up her own things as well as mine – and she's taking everything, mine and hers, back to Cambridge next week. Right now, though, she is clearly having a break and, from the way she's sitting, she's been there a while. She looks… pensive, I suppose, a touch of sadness in her eyes.

'I miss you, Scar,' she says softly.

I miss you too, I tell her. Because even though I'm here, I'm not really, am I? Not in the way that matters. But it's been a gift – one I didn't think I'd want – to be able to be around for the aftermath. To know that, however awful it was, the people I love *will* get through this.

Then Evie stands and disappears into my room. I could follow her, but I don't, because I'm not enough of a masochist to want to see it, sadly packed up, no longer mine. She comes back out, holding a picture frame. It is a photo of me, grinning at the camera, holding my arms wide on a beach. Crete. She took this, gave it to me on our first day of university, so that even if the first term was hard, I could remember the summer.

She sets the photo down on the desk, stares at it. Then she picks up her violin – the violin that has been sitting in this corner, waiting for her all this time. Her movements are shaky, and the tremor starts up when she moves the bow towards the strings. But she doesn't stop.

Instead she plays. She plays *our* song, and it is broken, the notes trembling, but it is there. She is playing and I am listening, and it is *ours*. Even after she starts to cry, tears tracing soft paths down her face, she keeps playing – right until the end. And it doesn't matter that she didn't play it at the funeral. Because she's doing it now, just for the two of us, the way this song always was.

And it hits me. *This* is it. The moment. It is not romantic, but it is no less powerful because of it. I'd spent so much of my life desperately searching for The One, moving from guy to guy, but I realize now I got it wrong. Maybe *the one* is just *that* person: the one who means more to you than anyone else, the one whose soul speaks to your own. And Evie is that person for me. She always was.

Chapter Forty

He's left. Evie had gone to Noah's house after she'd finished playing. Played for Scarlett, even though she wasn't around to hear it any more. Then she'd set the violin down and gone to find Nate. To tell him that she wanted to be with him. Because the only reason she *wasn't* doing that was because she was worried about what might happen – but something already *had* happened and it was too late to change that.

But she had been too late.

Evie let herself back in a little numbly, started up the stairs to her flat. She wouldn't be doing this for much longer. One week and she'd be out of London. It all seemed a little surreal.

She fumbled in her bag for her keys, looking down when she couldn't find them immediately. Which meant that, of course, she stumbled as she reached the top of the stairs, putting her hand out to break her fall and—

Another hand grasped hers. A warm, familiar hand.

Slowly she looked up from the hand, into his liquid brown eyes. Her heart stuttered. 'What are you doing here?' She was always asking him that, wasn't she?

He smiled, acknowledging that fact too.

'Astrid let me in,' he said, which didn't really answer the question. She glanced at the shut door on the opposite side of the corridor. She'd told Astrid that she was leaving, expecting there to be a bit of resentment, but Astrid had rolled her eyes: *That's what Zoom is for, come on!*

'I…' Her heart was beating, too fast. 'I went to your brother's house. He told me you'd left. For Australia.'

'I did leave.'

'But you're here.' *He's here, he's here.* The words circled around in her mind so that she couldn't think straight.

'Yeah, well, I turned round.' There was a suitcase next to him, she noticed now.

'You're not going?'

'I…'

'Or you are?' Evie said with a frown. 'You've come to say goodbye?' God, she couldn't handle it – not again. 'Because…' She took a breath, then spoke as quickly as she could, so that she couldn't stop herself. 'Because I think you should stay. I don't want you to go. I mean, I want…'

Still holding her hand, Nate pulled her gently towards him. 'I think I should go,' he said.

'Oh.' Her heart, so full of life a second ago, plummeted. 'Right, well—'

'But I think you should come with me.'

She stared at him. He stared at her.

'What?'

'I think you should come with me. To Australia.'

'You're serious.'

'I'm serious,' he said, nodding in confirmation.

'But I can't just…' She pulled her free hand through her hair. Why couldn't she? She'd already quit her job, already

327

agreed to leave the flat. She had nothing planned, beyond a vague idea of trying to find some tutoring work, which she could arguably do anywhere. 'Okay, say I do move to Australia with you.' *Australia – was she really saying this?*

'Okay,' Nate said with a grin. 'Say that. Let's go.' He made a movement as if to start down the stairs.

She put her hand on his chest. Beneath it, she could feel his heart beating – a quick, slightly erratic rhythm. A sign that he was not, even though he was pretending, quite so relaxed about this whole thing as he was making out. 'Say I do come,' she said, 'and then three months or six months or even two years down the line, you decide it's not what you want. Me there with you.'

'Well, the job's not for good, so we wouldn't be *there* indefinitely. We could come back to England and—'

'Nate.' Her voice was pleading now.

'Sorry.'

'I mean, what if you feel trapped, in a relationship? What if you resent me for it? And what if the MS becomes too much for you, despite what you say, and you—'

'Leave you?' He brushed a thumb over her cheek, and she nodded. Because it was stupid to pretend otherwise, stupid to pretend that it wasn't going to be a factor. Relationships were hard enough anyway, and she had this whole other problem to contend with.

'I won't,' he said simply.

'You can't promise that,' she whispered.

'No, I suppose I can't,' he said, his voice careful. 'But I can tell you this. I love you, Evie. And that's enough for me. *You're* enough – you're more than that.' His gaze locked on hers and she found she couldn't move, even if she'd wanted to. 'I meant what I said to you, that night. I've never wanted anything more than this.' His thumb traced a line down her cheek. 'That's still true.'

She had a flash of that night, enough to make her stomach tighten, before she remembered another conversation, outside on the pavement. *It's unpredictable. I'm unpredictable.* And maybe there was something in that. Maybe there was even beauty in unpredictability. Because it didn't only mean you didn't know what *bad* things were around the corner, it also meant you didn't know when there might be good things coming.

She took a breath. 'Okay.'

He blinked. 'Okay?'

'Okay.' A smile pulled at the edges of her lips. 'I'll come with you.'

For a moment he just looked at her, then he actually *whooped* and plucked her off her feet, spinning her in a circle in the tiny corridor, and Evie couldn't help it – she laughed.

He set her down, but didn't let go of her waist.

'And, well,' she said, 'I suppose if it doesn't work, then I'll figure something else out, one way or another.'

'We will.' He said it so firmly that she conceded.

'We will.' *One day at a time*, she told herself. Because that's all you could do, wasn't it? One moment after the next, making the best decision you could at any given time.

He pulled her to him, so that every inch of her was pressed against every inch of him. 'I love you, Evie Jenkins,' he said. And then he kissed her, lightly, but enough to make the heat in her core surge. He eased back a fraction. 'This is the part where you traditionally say it back.' He said it in a mocking tone, but she'd felt his heart. So she knew: he didn't only *want* to hear it, he needed to.

So she smiled against his lips. 'I love you, Nate Ritchie.' And this time it was her kissing him, and it was not soft, or light. She didn't care that anyone could walk into the corridor, could see them. They could be anywhere in this moment – and she felt that she *would* go anywhere, as long as it was the two of them.

Nate turned his attention to her neck, making her gasp, and because it felt so good to say it, she said it again. A promise, this time, as much as a statement.

'I love you.'

Chapter Forty-One

This time, when the memory of my death pulls at me, I do not fight it. I am back there, in that coffee shop near London Bridge. I am in the queue, the same harried-looking guy standing behind the counter. Something about this memory feels different from the others. Everything feels heightened – the smell of the coffee, the sound of the machine frothing milk, the cool air whisking in through the open doorway. Like my senses are all on high alert. Maybe it's to be expected, knowing what's to come, but everything feels more… *immediate*.

'What will it be?' the barista asks. And I know what happens next: I order a black Americano because I'm *stupidly* worried about the calories, when what I really want is a…

'Creme Egg latte.' The words are out there before I even realize what's happening.

I said that. Me. The *actual* me, not the me of memory. How is that possible? All those times I wanted to change something in the past and I couldn't, no matter how much I strained. And now here I am, on the day that I die, and I can… *Can I?* Can I change things?

I'm standing there, frozen in shock, when someone bumps into me. I remember this. I scowled, didn't look up. But I *do* look up, and a man in his fifties smiles down apologetically at me. I move out of the way and my body is back on track, moving without my input. I take out my phone, scroll through, linger on the message from Jason.

But I keep going, down to a message from Evie. *Me*, I'm doing this. It's like I have my body back, have *me* back.

I love you, Eves, I type quickly, unsure of how long this will last – how much time do I have, to control things, to change them? But I can't think of what else to say. What *do* you say, when you know you'll be dead in less than thirty minutes?

'Creme Egg latte!' The way the guy shouts it makes me realize it's not the first time he's said it. I send the message to Evie and scurry over to take the coffee off the counter, wish again for my sparkly coffee cup.

My mum's name flashes up on my phone screen as I step outside the coffee shop. 'Hi, Mum,' I say. Because I can answer. I'm not ignoring her, like I did last time.

'Hello, love, I was just wondering, for your—'

'I'm sorry,' I say quickly, because I can't do this. I can't have a conversation about a birthday that I'll never have – a birthday that has already happened, whether she knows it or not. 'I can't really talk, I've got to run, but I wanted to let you know I'm not ignoring you.'

Mum laughs. 'Don't be silly, love, we both know you regularly ignore me.'

My eyes are sparking with tears. I'm talking to her. I'm talking to my mum. 'Well, even if that's true, I still love you.'

I love you. It's the only thing that matters in the end, isn't it? It's the only thing to say.

Ahead of me, the pedestrian crossing is counting down, the big yellow numbers showing that there are three seconds left to get across. And just like before, I fumble the moment, so that I'm stuck on this side of the crossing, cars coming too fast, impatient to be on their way.

Then he's there. Some guy on a bright-red bike. Nate, wearing jeans and a jumper, no helmet.

He's one-handed – of course he is – holding the handlebars in the middle, the other hand holding his phone to his ear. And there's that laugh. I can't hear it over the traffic, but I don't need to. I know it so well by now.

I watch as he shoots past me, running through the lights literally the moment they turn from amber to red, without so much as checking over his shoulder.

It all happens again, exactly as it did that day. One of the oncoming cars beeping loudly. Nate jolting, swearing, out of the cycle lane.

The green man is beeping, the lights flashing. But I'm still watching him. Watching as he falls, head-first – and doesn't get up.

The memory has overwhelmed me again now, stripping away my control of myself, and I am running towards him, my coffee slurping through the small opening in the lid, heat searing my hand. I drop the cup completely, milky brown liquid seeping across the pavement like blood.

It's just before I reach the edge of the road that I pause. Remember that I changed my coffee order. Texted Evie.

Answered Mum. And I know: I could keep walking. I don't *have* to replay events exactly as they played out that day – I could leave it to chance. Maybe Nate will step into the road to get his bike and maybe Tasha will hit him, instead of me. But maybe not. Maybe we could *both* live.

One decision; it hits me how one decision has the power to change everything. And I'm remembering another decision I made – the one to get on the trampoline that day. The decision that led to me meeting Evie. How different my life would have been, without her.

I'm still hovering – nothing around me has moved, like the memory is holding its breath, waiting for me to make my choice. Are we always given a chance to change things, the day we die? Does everyone get to revisit it, to put things right? Did Nate's brother go through this: did he go through his suicide, all over again?

Nate. Telling Evie he loves her, like I knew he'd have to. She loves him back, doesn't she? He is the one for her, I know it. Will I remember, if I choose to keep walking right now? Will I be able to track Nate down, introduce him to Evie? It wouldn't be the same. It's only because of my death that they were forced together in quite that way – without it, he'd have no reason to try to help her and, through that, get to know her. They'd pass each other in the street and not think anything of it. And Evie…

Evie, playing that song for me. Playing music again, because of a string of events that was put into action after my death. Leaving London, going after what she wants. Will that happen, if I'm still alive?

I know then. There is only one choice. If I'd come back here – if I'd given in to the pull of the memory – sooner after I died, I would keep walking. But not now. Something has changed. Maybe I've changed. Isn't that ironic? Growing as a person after you die?

But maybe it's all irrelevant, anyway. Because maybe it's not even really a choice. Maybe it's just that you have to learn to accept it – realize that it is one thing in a chain of many events.

And so I take a breath, and as the world starts moving around me again, I give myself over to the memory – and I step off the pavement. Not because my life was meaningless, but because it was meaningful.

Because I *mattered*.

Acknowledgements

When I was trying (and failing) to start writing a book over ten years ago now, one of the things I'd do when I was struggling or giving up was write the acknowledgements in my head, for motivation, I think because that was the moment I was convinced it would feel real. And so, many years and a completely different book idea later, here goes…

Thanks, first and foremost, to my wonderful, supportive, smart, wise and just lovely agent, Sarah Hornsley, who has already had to deal with a range of ups and downs (probably more to come, sorry, Sarah), and without whom this book would definitely have been nowhere near as good as it (hopefully) is now. Thank you for your excitement for this idea, for giving me the motivation to keep going, and for being as excited as me when we got the deal. You are great.

Thank you to my brilliant editor, Sarah Hodgson, for your belief in this book and for your excitement that came through from the very first contact. (Also thank you for telling me it still made you cry second time through – sorry.) I know first-hand how many people it takes to get a book from that first idea through to a finished copy that you can actually hold because I've been the other side of the process, too. It takes so much hard work, dedication and passion from a whole team, and much of what goes on I'm sure I won't even know about. But huge thanks to Kate Straker, partly for giving me the chance to say 'my publicist', as opposed to it being the other way around, but also for your wisdom and support. Thank you to Felice McKeown and Sophie Walker in Marketing, for your creative ideas, enthusiasm and for being so incredibly organised and on it. Thank you to Mandy Greenfield, for your attention to detail and Hanna Kenne for all your work behind the scenes.

We've all heard the phrase 'don't judge a book by its cover', but in this case that is WRONG and I hope loads of people do just that, because I'm totally in love with it – thank you Holly Battle for the gorgeous cover, and for getting it right so immediately. I am in awe.

Georgina Moore (who, by the way, also has a book out right now) deserves huge love and thanks for a) taking me on a writing retreat to the Isle of Wight where I wrote a good chunk of this book and b) continuing to believe I'd have a book out there with my name on it, even when I didn't. Thank you, too, for your support, encouragement, and friendship over the last few years, both in writing and beyond.

I wrote this book with the support of The Novelry, an online creative writing school, who got me over the edge in my 'I can't do it' moments, got me going at a time where I was feeling very underconfident, and are chock full of writing support and wisdom. Thank you to Louise Dean and Katie Khan there, and extra special thanks to Emylia

Hall, for your support, enthusiasm, brilliant creative ideas and for making me inspired every time I spoke to you.

There are so many people who have had to put up with me saying I was going to/trying to write a book over the years, and who have offered support – both when things went right and when they very much didn't – encouragement and all-round belief that I could do it. So, thank you to my family – Ian, Jenny, Sally and Sophie Hunter; my friends – Laura Webster, Emily Stock, Lucy Hunt, Polly Hughes, Rosie Shelmerdine, Emma Harris; my publishing 'support group' – Naomi Mantin, Alison Barrow, Katie Brown, Becky Short, Millie Seaward, Jen Harlow, Phoebe Swinburn, and Sophie Christopher, who will never be forgotten; and the CBC group of 2015, Sean Lusk, Bill Macmillan, Jo Cunningham, Lynsey Urquhart, Robert Holtom, Sarah Shannon, Ella Dove, Charlotte Northedge, Ahsan Akbar, Victoria Halliday, Ben Walker, Georgina Parfitt, Paris Christofferson. Extra special thanks to Catherine Jarvie, for your unyielding support and cheerleading, for being more excited than me at various points of my writing journey, and for always being there to read something or talk writing when I need it.

And, of course, if you've read this far, then thank you – for picking up the book, and for reading until the end.